An ARIA Anthology

IN A
DARK
TIME

Selected Short Fiction,
Nonfiction, Poetry & Prose from
The Associastion of Rhode Island Authors

**In a Dark Time: Selected short fiction,
nonfiction, poetry & prose from The Association
of Rhode Island Authors; an ARIA Anthology**
Copyright © 2023 Association of Rhode Island Authors.
Entries are copyright © 2023 to their respective authors.

Produced and printed by Stillwater River Publications.
All rights reserved. Written and produced in the United States of America.
This book may not be reproduced or sold in any form without the expressed,
written permission of the author(s) and publisher.

Visit our website at
www.StillwaterPress.com
for more information.

First Stillwater River Publications Edition

ISBN: 978-1-960505-67-5

Library of Congress Control Number: 2023945169

1 2 3 4 5 6 7 8 9 10

A publication of the Association of Rhode Island Authors (ARIA).
Cover and interior design by Elisha Gillette.
Cover Photo Courtesy David Zapatka,
USA Stars & Lights, United States Lighthouse Society.
Published by Stillwater River Publications,
West Warwick, RI, USA.

*The views and opinions expressed
in this book are solely those of the author(s)
and do not necessarily reflect the views and opinions
of the Association of Rhode Island Authors (ARIA) or the publisher.*

Previous ARIA Anthologies

TABLE OF CONTENTS

FOREWORD

I'll admit, I had some doubts about this year's theme, "In a Dark Time." Would we have an anthology filled with gloomy, depressing stories and poetry? Had I made a terrible choice? Would our loyal readers give up, or turn back to our 2020 volume, "Hope," for a mood lift?

I needn't have worried. This year's anthology contains some of the best writing I've ever seen from ARIA members. It's why this year's volume is bigger—our judges wanted so many of the entries to be included, we agreed to fit in as many as we could.

"In a Dark Time" provided our writers with many options for interpretation—darkness can be viewed in a literal sense (nightfall), an emotional sense (the blues), or as a literary theme (good vs. evil). ARIA president Mike Squatrito asked members to "write about the things that haunt your subconscious." The optimistic writers in our group found the light, so don't worry—this anthology will give you everything—horror, grief, and misery, but also hope, forgiveness, and redemption.

Award-winning author Gail Eastwood's short story "The Redemption of Thomas" wowed the judges, and with the highest rating among her peers, she leads off the anthology. That story is bookended with "Slivers of Light" by Belle A. DeCosta, who won the judges' acclaim as well. And in between, you'll find beautiful poems, heart-wrenching narratives, and gorgeous essays. A huge thanks to ARIA member David Zapatka, whose amazing photograph of Beavertail Lighthouse in Jamestown graces our cover. And, as always, to Stillwater River Publications for professional production of this anthology.

We may be living in a dark time, but I'm reminded of a quote from former First Lady Michelle Obama: "Even when the world feels so dark, we're all trying to protect, kindle, and share the light we carry." Be well, and thank you for your continued support of the Association of Rhode Island Authors.

Martha Reynolds
Chair, ARIA Anthology
Association of Rhode Island Authors

IN A DARK TIME

THE REDEMPTION OF THOMAS

by Gail Eastwood

ENGLAND, 18__

The first woman I loved was my mother, of course. I barely remembered her, since she died when I was four. But I had loved her, or at least my idea of her, long after the dangers of childbirth had claimed her.

Scattered fragments resided in my brain, just a few images. One was the silent, darkened room where tears were not allowed (my father's voice commanding, "Hush, Thomas, you must not wake her."). Another was a gentle hand and a soft voice crooning soothing words ("There, there, my darling boy, it is only a bee sting") when the true issue wasn't so much the sting but my shock at discovering so small a thing could cause so much pain.

It was much later, at age 14, when I fell in love and discovered how much pain could come from larger things, like the human heart or the living people in our lives.

The source of that lesson was Cecily Hardcastle. Despite the image such a surname might conjure, she was a delicate, ethereal being who captured my heart from the first moment I saw her. I still cannot describe the feeling that struck me, as if she was goodness personified and some sort of salvation all rolled into it. I knew she was meant to be mine.

I never considered my father.

We first noticed her outside the British Museum where my father had brought me for a day of cultural edification during my Easter term break from school. It was a rare outing. My father had consigned me to the care of nannies for four years after my mother died, and then at age eight like many English boys of my social rank, I was sent off to Winchester, just another among quite a few lonely motherless boys.

In the six years since, Father and I had spent little time together. We were nearly strangers. But that day, at the instant we saw Miss Hardcastle descending from her carriage, a shared moment of unspoken but clear admiration passed between us.

She is a goddess.

She ought to have had blonde hair like some Botticelli Venus, but instead her tresses were raven, as dark as night, glossy as starlight. Black curls framed her face beneath her bonnet, creating the perfect contrast to her white skin and huge violet eyes. I had heard the term "rosebud mouth" before but it had never held any meaning until I saw hers. In truth, I had never paid much attention to women at all before that day. But I was quite certain then that no other woman walked the earth who could compare to her.

Fate had seemed kind that day, for we later came across her in one of the galleries. The mere sight of her set off tingling in my skin and an exuberant excitement coursing through my veins. Despite social convention that decreed a gentleman who had not been introduced should not speak to an unknown woman, my father was so bold as to make a comment on the exhibit she was studying intently. To this day I've no idea what he said, but the words made her laugh. And I swear an amused Miss Hardcastle was a vision so far beyond "goddess" that I had no words to describe her.

She and my father quite improperly began a conversation. That was the first moment I experienced a glimmer of what lay ahead for me. As they spoke, I ceased to exist, rendered invisible by their mutual interest, this young, incredibly special woman and my father, who had been a widower for ten years!

Of course, the term break ended and I was sent back to school. The occasional letter from home allowed me to glimpse the progress of my father's unlikely courtship of Miss Hardcastle. What did she see in him? I began to act out, venting my feelings on those around me. Fighting among the boys was not condemned, for it was all considered a part of the toughening process. But disrespect toward the instructors, tutors, or any others with authority over us was not to be tolerated.

It was inevitable, I suppose, that I was eventually sent down from Winchester. When I arrived at home, my father's face bore the darkest expression I had ever seen. Fury, insult, and disappointment warred there in an uncomfortable mix. But did he stop to think for even a moment about why my previously stellar behavior at school had changed so radically? Or ask? No, indeed not.

I struggled to keep my own face from mirroring his.

"Thomas, I need not tell you how unacceptable this is. That you have been sent down from school brings disgrace upon our family." His voice was thunderous yet still tightly controlled. "And of all the times to blacken our name, just when my courtship of Miss Hardcastle is progressing so well!"

As if blackening our name at some more propitious time would have served better.

"I suppose you are of an age now to be told certain realities of our situation. Our coffers are bleeding dry, and we badly need the replenishment an alliance with her family will give us. They possess considerable wealth, so in addition to all her more obvious charms, Miss Hardcastle is blessed with a very large dowry."

He paused to let this information sink into my brain, but all I felt was fury on her behalf that this circumstance even mattered to my father. Was not my love for her truer than his? I would have loved her even if she were the veriest pauper crawling in the gutter.

But my father was not finished. His brows drew together, making his dark expression even more fearsome. "I have been scraping to send you to Winchester, boy. Now that you have ruined your chances there,

I must call in whatever favors I can to have you accepted at Harrow or Rugby. Eton will never take you. How we shall cover the new tuition I have no idea other than to hurry Miss Hardcastle to the altar faster than I had planned."

Faster? *No, no, no!* Despair stabbed into my heart at his words. My own folly had brought about this disastrous turn.

The reaction must have shown on my face, for my father's tone shifted. "Do not worry that I don't love her, for I do."

Foolish man! How he misinterpreted me. But he hardly knew me. And I doubted that he knew what truly loving Miss Hardcastle felt like.

"I am not averse to marrying her sooner, not at all," he continued. "But I had not wished to rush her. I wanted her to have all the time she needed to come to know me and, I hope, love me. As your mother did."

Now his face showed some bleak sadness, and I wondered, had my mother loved him? And could Miss Hardcastle actually admire my father? He was handsome and titled, as I would be one day, but he was so much older! I knew him as little as he knew me, but the idea that a woman might be enchanted by him struck me as ridiculous.

Instead of sympathy, the thought sparked a tiny ray of unreasoned hope inside me. "What if she doesn't love you?"

My father sighed, ignoring my question in his usual way. "I do not want her to think I am marrying her for her money."

Even though you are. I wanted to shout it at him but clenched my teeth together to hold back the accusation. I dared not push his anger with me further.

*

I could not enroll at another school until the start of a new term. I remained at home, a silently suffering observer to my father's continued courtship. A hired tutor attempted to help maintain my studies and bore the brunt of my bad moods.

Miss Hardcastle no longer ignored me on the occasions when I was present, which was both balm to my soul and a torture as well, since I could see no way of declaring myself or claiming her heart. I was too young to marry even though only five years of age stood between us. And how would I convince her that my ardor was so rare and precious that she should wait for me? I felt helpless to fight the seemingly unstoppable forward push of events.

I was still at home the memorable day she and my father called me into the drawing room to make their announcement, their brilliant matching smiles filling the silk-clad room with the light of their happiness while casting my soul into utter darkness.

My father extended his benign smile to me. "Thomas, Miss Hardcastle has consented to make me the happiest of men by accepting my offer of marriage."

In assuring my father's happiness, she had damned me to my own version of hell. I felt hot, gaping blackness open up around me, threatening to swallow all that I was.

"We hope that we may have your congratulations and best wishes for our future."

Congratulate and wish them well? I knew what words I was expected to say, but I could not choke them out past the fossilized lump in my throat. My father had won. What was it she had seen in him? Or had she merely surrendered?

I could not force my face to reflect a happiness that existed nowhere in my universe. Trying not to stumble over the words, I muttered, "When do you expect to wed?"

It was the best I could do. Perhaps if they waited long enough, I could find some way to stop them.

She stepped towards me, driving my heart into a gallop. My eyes widened as I realized that she meant to touch me. Something almost like fear seized me at the prospect of such an intimate gesture. We had never been so close, ever. What if I spontaneously combusted in front of her?

"Dear Thomas," she said in a very gentle voice, slipping her fine long fingers around my hand. Heat shot up my arm and raced through the rest of my body, so hot that I actually looked to make sure my poor appendage was not actually flaming. "I hope you do not think I mean to supplant your mother, for I could never do so, and would never presume to try."

Perhaps my father's inability to read me was contagious.

Did she not know I could never see her as a mother figure? How could she even think such a thing, as close to me in age as she was?

She gave my fingers a little squeeze. "But I hope we may be friends."

*

When one's stepmother is as gentle and sweet as a fine summer breeze, being friends ought not to be difficult. However, when one is madly in love with her and in total despair that she has married one's father, that casts quite a sizeable rock into the matter.

The wedding happened while I was still at home. It was small and passed in a blur I barely recall, which makes me guess I was in some state of shock. Not long after, I was sent off to school again—Harrow, this time—in a darker frame of mind than ever.

I gained new friends quickly enough. Some admired the black cloud of hard anger that surrounded me, equating it with toughness. I think some felt being my friend offered protection, either from my own ire or the violence of others.

That was true to some extent. I welcomed any chance to employ my fists, and protecting my friends from other bullies gave me opportunities to vent my dark emotions while assuming a guise of humane benevolence. I grew more careful, this time, about when and how I lashed out. I maintained a tight control with those in authority.

My reputation as someone not to be trifled with grew. I cared not a whit for pain or bruises since they were nothing compared to the pain I nursed in my heart. Every letter from home (fewer than ever but each written in *her* flowing hand) poured salt into my wounds.

And then I received the one that made me feel as though a blade had ripped open my chest and carved my exposed and bleeding heart into slivers.

"Dear Thomas, your father and I are delighted to finally share with you the news that before long you will have a brother or sister. Need I mention that we are deliriously happy?"

Deliriously happy! Did the poor deluded woman not understand that this might be a death sentence? Did my father not recall how childbirth had killed my mother?

Fury darker and stronger than anything I had ever felt before flashed through my veins, so bleak it frightened even me. He was going to destroy her. And I—stuck a hundred miles way and still an underage schoolboy—could do *nothing* to save her. Would I be rendered helpless again? My rage rose up, but it did not carry me with it, for I was falling—falling backwards into the black abyss I had sensed before. This time I welcomed it.

*

Eventually I formed a plan. Going home became my entire focus. More fights, more misbehavior. I even frightened away my friends. I refused to study. Would they never decide to dismiss me? My tuition was already paid. But months passed with only warnings. I became so desperate, I considered setting fire to the headmaster's office. But concern that it could spiral out of control and do more harm than I intended stopped me. Perhaps I was not completely lost.

I sat in my small, darkened room at night, not studying, consumed by the idea that if I could just be at home, somehow my presence could prevent Cecily's death. I obsessed over the idea that my mother might have fought off death if only I had been allowed to climb beside her, reminding her she had a child who loved her and needed her to stay. The darkened room where tears were not allowed haunted me. "*Hush, Thomas, you must not wake her.*" My father had allowed her to go, when awakening her might have reminded her to live! I could not let his neglect cause the same mistake again.

Finally, finally, I was called before the headmaster once more. Apparently I had at last breached some limit of what could be tolerated at the school. I admit the old man was perceptive—he sensed that my unrelentingly horrid behavior might be motivated by some dark trouble haunting me. When I attempted to explain myself, however, he utterly failed to grasp the crisis of my soul. But at least he wrote to my father.

When Father arrived at Harrow more than a week later, he was furious. His black look greeted me in the headmaster's spartan, wood-paneled office. "You do understand, Thomas, that you've forced me to come here to tend to this matter when your stepmother's time could arrive early and I am not there?"

As usual, his anger and blame rendered me mute. I simply nodded and lowered myself into the seat the headmaster indicated. I was forced to listen as the man launched into a recital of all the misdeeds I had committed since my arrival at Harrow, related with a mixture of horror and bafflement on his face. The litany ended with his puzzled announcement, "Thomas fears you are going to kill your wife, my lord."

I had not stated it so baldly, but he was not wrong.

"We feel if he is delusional and this full of insensible rage then we are not able to provide here the discipline or structure that he requires."

Dear God. Were they going to consign me to Bedlam? I wanted to be sent home, not incarcerated with madmen. Unless I had become one. Was I mad? Would one know? *How* would one know? Just because part of me mired in the black abyss feared I had consigned myself to the devil? But I had not confessed that to anyone.

I might have unwittingly given my father the perfect way to be rid of me.

He aimed a look of perfect loathing at me. "Pack your things. We will return home as soon as possible. After the baby comes we will sort out what to do about you."

Reprieved! I could not disguise the relief that washed over me. I did not care about later. "Yes sir." Turning to the headmaster, I'm sure I must have presented an eagerness that shocked him. "Am I dismissed, sir?"

"Indeed you are, young man. From this office and from this school."

*

I had not considered how the reports of my abhorrent behavior might affect Cecily's feelings about me. She floated through the house like a ship in full sail, happy and expectant except when she saw me. At the rare times I was not banished to my room or buried within the welcome sanctuary of our large library, her beautiful violet gaze rested on me with sadness and disappointment that hurt far more than my father's predictable anger. I had lost any good opinion she might once have had about me.

But I still loved her.

"Was it only that you did not wish to be at school, Thomas?" she asked me one day when we met in the passage outside the door of the library. No preamble was required, for we both knew what she referred to. Two dismissals from two prestigious schools. "I would so like to understand. I don't believe you are that terrible boy. Would it not have been sufficient to simply write to your father and tell him?"

I shook my head, staring down at my feet, embarrassed that her gentle questioning had made tears prick my eyes. As soon as I had blinked them away, I looked at her. My anger over the marriage seemed entirely irrelevant now. And only the most recent bout of raging behavior had been deliberate. How could I possibly explain?

I love you. I wanted you to be mine. I am afraid for you now. No, it could not be said, or understood. She might also think me mad.

"It is complicated," I settled for instead, shaking my head again. "I am truly sorry for all the trouble I caused."

"However? I believe I heard a 'however' behind those words."

Something my father would *never* have heard. The next words blurted out of my mouth in an uncontrolled rush. "Please, please just promise me you won't die—when the baby comes."

I dashed into the haven of the library and closed the door behind me, blocking out the view of her beautiful, astonished face, not waiting to see if enlightenment also dawned there. Even if she might now recognize the danger she faced or have a glimpse into the torture of my twisted soul, there was nothing to be done about any of it. Nature would follow its inevitable course, the birth would proceed. Life and death would hang in the balance.

The final hurdle was to find some way to be present, either during the birthing time or immediately afterwards. I still harbored the sense that my presence somehow would make a difference—could prevent the tragic outcome that had taken my mother away. If the baby's arrival killed Cecily, was I black-hearted enough to kill the child? Such an exchange of lives could not be accepted! Prevention was the key that could save me from such a test. But how would I ever convince my father to allow me anywhere near his wife at such a delicate time? Especially as by now at least *he* must be certain I belonged to the devil.

In the following days I noticed a change in my stepmother's attitude towards me. Instead of sadness and disappointment, her gaze when it rested on me seemed full of speculation, as if she were still wrestling with the significance of my few words to her. I regained a little of my visibility in the household, now being allowed to dine *en famille*, although most of the conversations still bypassed me. I hoped my silent company would be taken for obedience by my father and might earn acceptance if not approval.

One night the tattoo of hurried footsteps and murmur of excited voices in the passage outside my door aroused me from deep slumber. As I lay half-awake, an excruciating wail split the night and banished any remaining sleep from my brain. My blood turned to ice.

Kicking away the covers and racing to my door, I poked out my head. One of the maids hurrying by paused long enough to explain, "'Tis the mistress. Her babe is comin'. They've sent Peter for the midwife."

Peter was an under-footman, and the midwife was the closest thing to a physician to be had in the country village near our estate. Fancy doctors could only be found in large cities like Bath or London. We had a London house. If only we were there!

Our housekeeper was following behind the maid who had spoken. Something in my face must have touched her, for she spoke to me kindly. "Remember this is simply nature taking its course, Master Thomas. But if you want to help, you could pray."

Could I? Would there be any point? After the black rage that had consumed me and the pain I had inflicted on others in my anger, would any god of mercy still listen to me? Certainly the devil would only laugh at the fear consuming me now.

I lit no lamp, preferring to sit on my bed enshrouded in the close darkness, listening to whatever sounds reached me. Cries of pain, the arrival of the midwife. The darkness hid my dread and shame. Eventually a prayer rose up: "Dear God, if you are there and if you hear me, please save Cecily. Not for me. Not for my father. Save her because the world needs her goodness. And her baby will need her. Please do not rob another child of its loving mother the way I lost mine."

I stopped, wondering if God would be offended that I had accused him of robbery. I began again. "Please save her child, also." If Cecily lived and her child did not, she would be devastated, and I could not want that pain for her. But I didn't know any reason that God should listen to me.

More wails penetrated the dark womb of my chamber. Why was it that humans must come into this life causing pain for others, and continue the practice all through their lives?

"Without the darkness, there is no light."

I would have sworn the voice I heard was real, but there was no one in the room with me. It catapulted me, trembling, off my bed and out into the lit passage beyond my door.

My father slumped against the wall outside the door of Cecily's bedroom some twenty paces away from me. Without his usual rigid posture and air of unquestioned authority, he seemed a different creature altogether from the father I knew. *Vulnerable, human.* He looked up as I emerged, his face lined with age and worry. Some of those creases had most certainly been put there by me.

"She is having a hard time of it, Thomas, but they assure me that all will be well." He spoke quite as if he conversed with me regularly. That he would turn to me now—see me, share something with me—told me how deeply concerned he was.

"Do you believe them, sir?"

"I do. I have to. I—I could not bear to go through this again."

Our agony united us. "You must keep her awake then, Father. Do not let her drift away like my mother."

He straightened as if in shock, just as another wail erupted from behind the door across from him. He spoke sharply. "You remember that?"

I nodded curtly. "You kept me away from her. You were afraid my crying would disturb her."

He rubbed a hand over his face. "Dear God, I never imagined you might remember. You were so young!"

"I wanted to remind her of why she should live. But you wouldn't let me. You let her die."

He bowed his head and shook it slowly. "We could not have saved her, either of us. She had suffered a hemorrhage and lost too much blood. You were too young to understand. I didn't think you would remember."

I stared at him. "I blamed you."

He stared down at his clasped hands. "I never knew. I'm sorry." Raising his head with apparent effort, he fixed on me a gaze as bleak as I had ever seen. He was a broken man unrecognizable to me. "I didn't know how to manage after I lost her. So I lost you, too."

Another wail sounded, this time more emphatic. There was energy behind it, and it rose and then cut off. And moments later, another wail. But this one was more like a shimmering cry of discovery and surprise, the sound of new life coming into the world of light.

The door opened, and my father was called into the room. Left alone in the passage, I took up my father's position leaning against the wall. There might be no point in staying there, but I would wait all the same.

Hardly a few moments could have passed before the door opened again, however. My father stood there, looking utterly serious, and my heart dropped.

"No, Thomas—thank the Lord they are both fine. And she would like you to come in. *We* would. You may see for yourself."

I took a moment to let the relief surge through me and uncurled my tightened fingers. Pushing off from the wall, I crossed the space between us, a few steps merely, but in truth a huge distance. *I had been invited in!* I entered the inner sanctum as my father held the door open for me.

Cecily presided from her bed, clean linens already tucked around her. She looked both exhausted and radiant, more beautiful than ever, holding a swaddled bundle that could only be the babe. Our housekeeper and the midwife hovered nearby, beaming as if they had done all the work of birthing it themselves.

"Thomas, come and meet your sister." Cecily's voice was soft and a little strained, as if pushing the words out took great effort.

At my hesitation, she smiled. A thousand beams of sunlight filled the room. "I am well. You must trust me. I am just tired. Amelia did not make her entrance easily."

So I approached, walking past the other women. My father followed close behind me. Cecily cradled the baby against one arm and pulled back some of the wrappings so I could see her. "As her elder brother, one day you may be responsible for her well-being, Thomas."

Her brother. The connection had not truly struck me until that moment. I had never had a sibling, never wondered about my mother's lost baby, nor ever been part of what could be called a family.

My world quaked and shifted. Was it too late to change?

I leaned in so I could truly see this small being of tremendous power. Wrinkled and red, she did not remotely resemble the angelic cherub I expected. What did I know about newborns? Still, something was special about her. Tiny she was, with dark hair like her mother, and a rosebud mouth. One day soon, I would wager, she might have violet eyes. But if she never did, it would not matter. She would be beautiful her own way.

"Would you like to hold her, Thomas?"

No! Did I dare? What if I dropped her? I glanced at my father expecting stern disapproval, but he nodded encouragement, smiling.

"Just hold her like this, with one hand to support her head." Cecily handed her over, trusting me. Could I trust myself?

As I leaned close to Amelia, a tiny hand appeared above the fold of cloth across her chest, each infinitesimal finger perfect, reaching, grasping, ready to explore this new life.

With the wave of that small hand, the pieces of my shattered heart seemed to knit back together, as if offered some kind of absolution. The black abyss disappeared—vanquished by the light of love surrounding me.

That's all it took to banish the darkness. It seems I merely needed to learn a new kind of love—for a family who wanted me, for a child who might need me. And in that moment I did, standing between my stepmother and my father, holding their baby in my arms. It was not too late. Maybe it never is.

"Welcome to the family, Amelia," I said, trying out this new idea. *Welcome to the family, Thomas.*

A Rhode Island native living in South County and an Anglophile from an early age, **Gail Eastwood** is the award-winning author of "sweet/low heat" romance fiction set in the English Regency period. Her work, detailed on her website (www.gaileastwoodauthor.com) is generally lighter in tone than Thomas's story, but the theme inspired her!

WHEN I WALKED IN THE DARK

by A. Keith Carreiro

when i walked in the dark
  black smothering scintillating
    through my eyes
      i saw people as flashes in air
        pinpricks of light
          that were born and died
            that lit and sprayed
              as a lightning fan
                being twitched by some
                  shadowy hand

                    then one moment in space
                      one brief brushstroke of
                        time things became the
                          opposite of what they were
                            i walked in light and people
                              were flashes of dark and
                                the hum and love of life
                                  kindled

and we laughed and cried
making love in the mountains
the oceans and the air and never
did we touch the hand of sadness
though there was pain when i
left you and you said goodnight
sweet prince —

A. Keith Carreiro started writing poetry in high school. Reading, music, storytelling, and movies became some of his major passions, all of which set him on a lifelong path of exploration in creativity. For him, poetry forms the basis upon which all imagination and storytelling unfold.

STILL FRAME

by David Boiani

I t's been one month to the day since my mother passed away from cancer. It had been a grueling, four-year battle with not only heart-breaking and numerous trips to the ER, but also the hope and joy of experiencing her return home, each time ready for another encounter with what was to come next. Finally, she was taken from us at the much too youthful age of sixty-one. I could say that I was ready for it, however, I've found that to be incorrect. You're never truly ready. Prepared maybe, but hardly ready. Oddly enough, the hardest part isn't the moment you find out or the ceremonies that follow, it's when you settle back into your life and realize the unique ways the departed had touched your life are gone forever. Seeing their name on your cell when they called and hearing their voice, eager to catch up on your lives. Reminiscing about memories shared that only you knew about. Having a thought flash into your mind about what gift you should purchase as their birthday approaches before you're suddenly brought back to reality and realize they're gone. Those are the moments that sting. I haven't made up my mind on what I believe about the afterlife and I've never been religious. However, what pushes me forward in those awful moments of heartache and pain is accepting that death comes for us all and we'll all join the black parade soon enough. Hopefully we'll be with our loved ones and remember them as our spirit floats from this world to the next. We must enjoy our limited time left here, for when that day comes, we'll have all eternity to rest.

*

I haven't thought about the camera much since her passing. Grieving takes up much of your energy and brain function and I've been so busy getting the domestic and legal proceedings in order that there wasn't much time or mental capacity left for much else. The device I'm referring to is an old Polaroid 600 square instant camera. You know the type: you click a button and the square film slides out of the front end and the picture magically appears fifteen to thirty minutes later. I have reasons to believe our version of this camera was special. However, I'm getting ahead of myself. Let me take you back thirty-five years to when I was a young boy.

*

On a beautiful late spring Friday night in June of '85, my father pulled into our driveway at his usual time of 6:30. I was a seven-year-old boy at the time and sports had become an important part of my life already. My friend and I had erected a basketball rim with a homemade wooden backboard screwed into a telephone pole on the end of my street. We lived on a dead-end street with a large pond directly to the northeast. We both looked up quickly as my father waved before entering our humble home. My mother and sister were inside and when I came in about an hour later, I saw the gift my father had brought home for the family: a brand-new Polaroid 600 square instant camera. I blinked my eyes as a flash momentarily blinded me. My mother smiled as a square piece of film slid out into her hand. She'd always wanted one and seemed like a kid on Christmas morning after opening a new toy.

"Isn't that cool?" she said as she waited with the white square held in front of her.

"Mom, if you shake it in the air, it develops quicker," my sister added.

"No, silly, that's just a misconception."

"What's a misconception?" I asked.

"It means it isn't real, dummy," my sister responded.

"I didn't ask you, moron," I fired back.

"You two stop it and come look at this."

We huddled around our mother as my image slowly came into focus. At first it was bland and foggy with just my outline visible; however, seemingly by the minute my face came into focus.

"Wow, that's awesome," I said.

"Mom, why didn't you take my picture?" my sister said as she stormed off into the living room to watch television. Two years older than me, she'd recently discovered MTV and it had become her chosen viewing pleasure to pass the time. My mother put the camera away and resumed preparing dinner for us. I didn't know it at the time, but that camera would prove to be a substantial part of our family's life in the following decade. It would be there through the birthdays, Thanksgivings, Christ-mases, Halloweens, sporting events, school plays, musicals, and award nights. My mother had a suitcase that she'd fill with Polaroids from our biggest events and memories. I wouldn't realize how magical that camera really was until years later when she became ill, and I stumbled on the suitcase accidentally.

*

As I've stated, my mother had been on a grueling routine of ER visits, hospital stays, and doctor's appointments. During one of the many prolonged stays in the hospital, I visited her place to pick up some things. After loading up a few books, her phone charger, and crossword puzzles, I headed to her closet to grab a sweater as she was always chilly while staying at the hospital. I noticed in the corner on the floor the old suitcase that contained our family's Polaroids. In a moment of curiosity and nostalgia, I lifted it and placed it on the bed, clicked the latches open and lifted the upper half. As I gazed into the treasures of my past, the memories came rushing back. One at the beach of my sister and me swimming in the ocean together, one from my Little League championship season of me holding the team trophy, and one of my first pet, a golden retriever named Cooper. I reached in and grasped Cooper. The picture felt cold and smooth under my fingers. Cooper was sitting back with a look of contentment on his face. He was splashed in sunlight and his coat was shiny and bright, the rays bringing out his beautiful color. I placed the picture down on the bed and with my fingertips traced the outline of his head and body. I threw my head back in memory as each finger came to rest, all connected to this moment in time from my past. Then something happened that I can't explain because it doesn't fall into the possibilities set forth by the physics of our earth. I suddenly felt a charge of energy run through my body and for a few moments I was suspended in time, frozen as the wave of energy subsided.

I opened my eyes and there in front of me was Cooper, wagging his tail as he jumped up at me. We were in our old yard at exactly the same spot the picture was taken so many years ago. I reached down with my arms and hugged my old friend and his tongue was soon bathing my face and I laughed a child's laugh, natural and pure. I glanced down and noticed my old Converse sneakers that I wore as a boy. It was a hot summer day with a refreshing breeze and the scents from my old yard of lilac and pine came rushing back, connecting to memories in my brain from so long ago. The bright sunshine sparkles off the clear water of the lake next to our yard. Cooper jumped again, knocking me down and I lay on my back with my face wet from his kisses until I returned to my mother's bedroom moments later.

The whole sequence took about twenty seconds. I fell back, lost my footing and hit my head on her dresser as I attempted to regain my bearings and figure out what the heck had just happened. I scrambled back to my feet and looked into the suitcase. I visited a dozen moments in time that day before locking the suitcase and putting it away. As thrilling as the experience was, it scared me not knowing a rational reason how it was possible. I've never been one to believe in magic or anything that couldn't be explained by science or mathematics; however, that day changed me forever.

*

You may wonder why the occurrence hadn't been discovered before and my answer is how often does anyone touch a photo with the tips of all five fingers? I simply stumbled onto the phenomena. My next course of action was to search frantically for the camera. I found it tucked in a bag in another corner of the same closet. I then googled the film and discovered it was still available. I ordered a few boxes and had them expressed to me overnight. To my chagrin, when I received the film, loaded the camera and attempted to take a picture of my backyard, the camera wouldn't work. I thought about getting it repaired but I didn't want to risk changing the orientation of everything involved. I mean, what if I had it repaired and the same circumstances that made the phenomena possible somehow changed? Ultimately, I decided it wasn't worth the risk. There were hundreds of memories I'd yet to experience and I wasn't going to jeopardize that. I pushed the camera and the pictures to the back of my mind. My mother was front and center of importance at the moment and there was still a battle to be fought.

*

My mother's health slowly deteriorated. Anyone who's fought the cancer battle with a loved one understands the grueling battle of ups and downs, good days surrounded by bad days, and watching them suffer. Soon the positive moments were devoured by the negative and she was living a grisly existence. One afternoon on a bright spring day the hospital called and said her condition had deteriorated and we needed to come in. She passed the next day under a heavy dose of morphine.

*

Today, the memories of my mother are never far from my mind. My life has settled enough to bring back thoughts of the polaroid and the magical pictures. I picked up the suitcase a few weeks after her passing and it now sits open in front of me on my kitchen table. I pick up a picture of my mom standing in front of the lake. It must've been early fall as the leaves had just started to turn. She had a cup of coffee in her hand, a wide smile on her face and a happy, content look in her eyes. My guess is that I was seven or eight at the time. I reach down, press my fingertips onto the picture and close my eyes...

A rush of energy comes over me then settles, and I open my eyes to a bright, crisp, sun-splashed morning. My mother looks radiant, full of life with a sparkle in her eyes and a healthy body full of energy. I had forgotten how she looked in those times. I run up to her, a young boy full of love for his mother. I wrap my arms around her as a bit of coffee spills onto the grass below. She laughs and I feel her arms around me. I hold on tight for the remaining moments. The last thing I remember is seeing the coffee mug she had dropped so she could hug me back.

I return to the present and drop my face into my hands as the tears flow without restraint. I've always held in my emotions, even through the most difficult of times in life. I let go and cry steadily for three or four minutes until I regain my composure. I dry my eyes and notice I'm still holding the picture, which is damp from my tears. This is how I wanted to remember her, vibrant and full of life. Seeing her happy and alive doesn't make letting her go easy, but it helps dull the pain. I set the picture down and scour the pile of pictures for ones of my mother. I visit her in dozens of moments frozen in time before I feel content. I close the suitcase and go to bed. Memories of times past fill my dreams.

*

Life continues on. The pain never goes away but it has dulled as I get buried in my life's routines again. We always return to life's twenty-first century cycle of work: sleep, eat, rinse and repeat. My mind and heart always go back to my mother, and I found myself with the suitcase open in front of me on a lonely Saturday night. I dig deep to the bottom of the pile of memories and uncover a picture that instantly brings me back to the time and place forever immortalized by the layers of grains, dyes, and materials used to create the picture. I rise from the table, grab my winter jacket in the back of the foyer closet, slide into it and return to my seat. I close my eyes and touch all five fingertips on the smooth surface.

I feel the dramatic change in temperature as I open my eyes to a steady snowfall being blown by a brisk breeze. My sister and mother are by the side of the pond, which has frozen over to create an ice rink covered by new-fallen snow. I hear the singing as we all step out onto the winter wonderland. It's Christmas Eve and we're singing Christmas carols. We're happy just to be here in the moment on this glorious night with the people we love.

The moment is gone as quickly as it appeared and I'm back in my house, sitting at my kitchen table. I think about my sister and how she's struggled with our mother's death, and I decide it's time. Time to share my secret with her. Time to share our memories once again. I pick up my phone and dial her number.

*

She arrives a few hours later, her curiosity feeding her swift response. I simply told her that I had a surprise, and she needed to be physically present to witness and understand it. After a half-dozen attempts to grind the mysterious secret out of me, she huffed and said she was on her way. She now sits at my kitchen table with a mug of fresh-brewed coffee and the closed suitcase in front of us.

"Do you remember the old Polaroid camera that Dad brought home one day? The one Mom used for all of our childhood memories?"

I feel her puzzlement as her eyes dart between me and the case.

"Sure, she had that camera everywhere we went," she finally replies.

"Right. This suitcase contains all the pictures she kept from those times."

I click the case open and sit back to watch her shuffle through our memories.

"Wow, there must be a thousand pictures here."

After a few minutes of reminiscing about the moments, settings, and memories in front of us, she turns to me and says, "Thank you for sharing this with me."

I smile. "That isn't the surprise. I need you to clear your head and forget whatever it is you thought about the physics of this world."

I glance up to see if she thinks I've lost my mind and the look on her face confirms my expectations.

"It would probably be better if I just show you."

I shuffle through the pictures until I find the Christmas Eve setting. I hold it in front of us for a few moments as I take in the magical moment caught in a still frame for eternity. I place it on the table.

"Put on that jacket," I say as I point to my winter coat. She looks at me like she's deciding whether or not to admit me to the local loony bin before she finally relents and does as I ask. "Now, just relax and let me show you." I take her hand in mine and place it on the photo, connecting the tips of her fingers one by one until I feel the energy surge through her. I watch her as an expression of awe dominates her face. A moment later she is gone. I check my wristwatch and watch the seconds go by. At the twenty-second mark she reappears. She looks at me as tears stream down her face. For the next thirty seconds nothing is said between us. I know she's simply processing the experience just as I did the first time I took the leap. Finally, she gets up out of her chair, walks over to me and throws her arms around me. Nothing more needs to be said. I know this is her way of telling me that she loves me.

"Still Frame" is dedicated to the loving memory of my mother.
David Boiani lives in Coventry, Rhode Island. He writes psychological thrillers mixed with a touch of horror. He has two short story collections available, *Dark Musings* and *Darker Musings*. His debut novel, *A Thin Line* and its sequel, *The Redemption*, are also now available as is his latest offering, *Immortal*.

THE SONG OF DARKNESS

by Kevin Duarte

Qu'Tkar swam twenty meters beneath the waves of the Drengali ocean. He pulled the water with his arms, sending his body racing past thick patches of kelp and seaweed, and over mounds of coral reef. He looked up and saw the brilliance of the faintest blue sky above him, decorated with a scatter of smoldering white clouds. He rose to two meters from the surface, where he could feel the heat as the gentle waves seared into mist, then disappeared altogether into the sky. The oceans of Drengali were shallow. His people had yet to discover a place with water more than thirty meters deep. But the sea was enough to provide and protect them, which they needed, because Drengali was surrounded by seven stars.

Qu'Tkar pulled hard, his tired legs kicking as he shot to the surface and broke the waterline. His secondary eyelids closed to protect him from the blinding light of the five-star sky. He saw Najak, the large blue star, hanging low to the north next to Zeri, its smaller red sister. Ferius, a blue star like Najak, but much smaller, was high in the sky but very far away. Sketerus, a cooler orange star much larger than Ferius, sat next to Najak. Phoberus and Felix, the twin yellow stars twice the size of Zeri, were hidden behind the far side of the planet. Qu'Tkar knew they would appear later in the cycle, spinning relentlessly around each other in a fiery binary dance.

At the center of it all was Ebuutan, the red giant star around which all objects traveled. Fifty times larger than any of the other stars, it alone bathed Drengali with enough light and heat to sustain life on the planet. The addition of the sister stars inflicted the planet with copious amounts of searing heat and blinding radiance as they bathed Drengali in perpetual, life-giving light.

Qu'Tkar peered across the surface toward the dry, lifeless stretch of arid desert to the west. An explorer at heart, he had navigated the above world several times, walking until the heat of the suns dried his gills and seared his skin to the point of near suffocation, forcing him to retreat into the Drengali ocean and the waters that sustained him. His legs were more equipped to propel him through the ocean than support his weight, but Qu'Tkar trained hard, and over time his legs grew stronger, allowing him to extend the duration of his treks across the above world. He was unsure what he was looking for on his journeys, but he felt deep within him the above world had something for him to find.

Qu'Tkar dove under the water and arrived at his destination. He swam toward a group of fellow students gathered among the decorative coral structures of the ocean floor. At the front of the group were the Magisters that taught them.

"Last time we met, we sang the *Song of Creation*," greeted Magister Qu'Fashell. "Today my wife Qe'Shastair will begin to teach you the *Song of Replenishing.*"

"Bodies to sit and ears to hear," added Qe'Shastair as she clapped her hands for attention.

Qu'Tkar and the students sat on the ocean floor, their focus on the Magisters. The class was limited to a dozen students, for the instructors knew the importance of ensuring the students knew the songs intimately; otherwise the knowledge shared through them risked being lost forever.

Qe'Shastair closed her eyes and tilted her head back the slightest bit, then began to sing. The sound of her voice, like the voices of all the people of Drengali, rolled through the water in rhythmic waves.

The waters of life upon the land
Spread evenly by Ebuutan's hand
Turned to vapor and raised on high
Scattered across Drengali's sky
Casting shadows across the world
While Ebuutan's great light unfurled
The clouds themselves be made to burst
Quenching all Drengali's thirst

The Magister opened her eyes as if she had returned from a trance.

"That was beautiful," said Qu'Fashell with a nod and a smile. "Your singing sends the most pleasant waves through Drengali's oceans." He turned to the students. "The *Song of Replenishing* speaks of the rains that fill our seas. Although the clouds that bring them cast a forbidding shadow, the radiance of Ebuutan and the sister stars penetrate the clouds to bathe us in their perpetual, life-giving light."

"Are the seven stars all that be?" asked Qu'Tkar.

"That, and Drengali of course," replied Qu'Fashell.

"But what if there were more?"

"By the Songs!" replied Qe'Shastair as she and the students gasped. "Do you see more than seven stars in the Drengali sky?"

"No," Qu'Tkar replied, lowering his head. He nervously scratched a line in the sea floor, sending sand floating upwards, which slowly fell back onto the sea floor, erasing the mark. "But I see things that make me think there could be more."

"Sing us these songs and enlighten us," urged Qe'Shastair.

"The things I speak of are not contained within songs," replied Qu'Tkar, huffing. "I see the way things work all around us."

"Explain this to us," pressed the Magister.

"The *Song of Replenishing* tells us how the oceans of Drengali are filled by the rains," started Qu'Tkar. "The oceans then provide for the plants, which feed the creatures that provide for us. All of which starts with Ebuutan, which turns the oceans into clouds that fuel the rains."

"Of course," replied Qe'Shastair. "The power of Ebuutan causes this to be."

"But what provides for Ebuutan?" asked Qu'Tkar.

The Magisters and students gasped in unison.

"There is no greater power than Ebuutan," rebuked Qu'Fashell. "When you look up through the waters of the ocean, do you see anything greater than Ebuutan?"

"No," replied Qu'Tkar. "I respect the power of Ebuutan." He continued in a subdued, careful tone. "But sometimes I feel the light of Ebuutan is so bright it blinds us."

"Heresy!" shouted Qe'Shastair, stirring the water around her. "The light of Ebuutan is all revealing. There is nothing it would hide from us. There is nothing more than what we see. We have Drengali, and the seven stars above it. What more do we need?"

Qu'Tkar suppressed any rebuttals that came to mind. The Magisters reigned over the class like Ebuutan reigned over the Drengali sky, and he knew his instructors' fury could burn just as deeply. The last thing Qu'Tkar needed was word of his verbal insurrections being sung throughout his people, eventually finding their way to his parents.

Quietly, almost rhetorically he added, "I just think there is more."

Qu'Fashell heard the remark, swam to his student, and placed an arm around his shoulder. He spoke in a calm but cautionary voice. "Be careful not to cast a shadow between yourself and the sun that shines upon you."

Qu'Tkar slowly turned his head toward his instructor and sighed.

"Come, let us learn another of Drengali's songs," urged Qe'Shastair to break the tension.

Another song was sung, then the class was dismissed. Set free, the students left in haste. Some looked back at Qu'Tkar, shaking their heads as they swam away. He tried to ignore them, kicking his legs to propel himself through the water as he headed home.

*

"Good cycle to you, my son," greeted Qe'Lashar, his mother. She sang as she prepared the kelp she gathered from her garden, the song instructing her in the recipe.

"Good cycle to you, Mother," replied Qu'Tkar as he entered the dwelling. Located fifteen meters below the surface of the sea, it consisted of coral covered in seaweed and algae, along pockets of kelp that floated vertically in the water.

"How are your studies coming along?" she inquired.

"I have learned more of the songs," Qu'Tkar replied. "About how Drengali came to be."

"The *Song of Creation*," she replied with delight. "Sing it to me."

"Oh, Mother," he rebuked.

"Qu'Tkar, these songs are our history and our knowledge," she replied sternly. "To know them is to know not only Drengali's past, but its cumulative knowledge as well."

Qu'Tkar huffed, turning his head. He swiped the sandy ground with his hand, watching the small particles as they danced and swirled around his fingers. Slowly they fell back to the sea floor. Inhaling water past his gills, he coaxed himself to sing.

After Ebuutan came to be
It shed a piece of self for thee
Rock and matter came to rest
'Round seven stars, the fiery test
Replenishment - the saving storms
Caused oceans shallow, seas to form
Creatures thrived beneath the waves
A million lives the waters saved
Forever locked in Ebuutan's space
Drengali feels the light's embrace
Six star sisters forever roam
Their dance 'round Ebuutan is flown

Providing with its awesome might
The gift of everlasting light

Qe'Lashar smiled and clapped her hands, sending waves through the water. "That was wonderful! You are learning more and more songs, Qu'Tkar. Soon you will be filled with more songs of Drengali than your father and me."

"What is the point, Mother?" Qu'Tkar replied.

His mother covered her mouth, then snapped back. "Qu'Tkar? How can you ask such a thing?"

"The songs are the knowledge of our people. They are crucial to who we are," replied Qu'Glator as he entered the room. He kissed his wife and handed her a small kelp sack. "Without them, we would forget our history and accomplishments."

Qu'Tkar lowered his head. "But why songs, Father? There must be a better way to retain the knowledge, even expand upon it?"

"The rhythm and meter of songs are easier to remember than just words, my son," replied Qu'Glator. "But if you were to devise a way for such knowledge to be stored, you would be forever revered in song. Many of our ancestors have tried. They devised symbols and etched them onto the sea floor, carved them into the coral reefs, and scratched them into kelp. But the sea relentlessly washes away any traces. That is why our ancestors long ago began crafting and singing the songs of Drengali. If it were not for the songs, we would surely forget what we have learned over the generations."

"I understand," conceded Qu'Tkar. "How many songs do you know, Mother?"

"I am versed in over a thousand," she said, smiling. It was a source of pride for her. "But your father knows even more."

"Is this true?" inquired Qu'Tkar.

Qu'Glator laughed, a burst of bubbles expelling from his mouth. "Yes, it is true. But I would rather hear your mother's singing travel through the oceans of Drengali than mine. But let us not talk of such things just yet, my son. Dinner is ready, and I, for one, am hungry."

Qe'Lashar cleared a piece of coral that made up the dinner table, then placed an assortment of small, hard-shelled mollusks upon it. Retrieving one, Qu'Tkar took a sliver of stone shaped like a small spear and freed the abductor muscle from the shell. He looked at the clean white flesh, then popped the creature into his mouth. As he chewed, he looked at a small school of fish that swam nearby, their eyes scanning. One of the fish saw a piece of flesh floating in the water. It kicked its tail, swam into the chamber, plucked the morsel, then swam away.

"Why do we not eat fish?" asked Qu'Tkar as he placed his spear on the table. His father shucked the flesh from a long, black shell, then, staring down the opportunistic fish hovering nearby, guided the flesh into his mouth. A fish raced to the discarded shell, diving and probing it with his mouth.

"Have you forgotten the *Song of Feasting*," replied Qe'Lashar. Closing her eyes, she inhaled deeply and sang, the water flowing from her mouth in pulsating waves that carried every word.

Drengali dressed in peace and love
Fueled by Ebuutan above
Its creatures living large and small
Shall never made by hands to fall
If fin or limb or eyes we share
Their bodies we shall always spare
There shall never be the need to kill
As was Ebuutan's goal and will
The ocean provides for all our need
Plants and mollusks upon which to feed
Let peace reign forever throughout the world
The light of seven stars unfurled

"Beautifully sung," remarked Qu'Glator. His wife turned to him and smiled.

"How was your lesson with the Magisters?" she asked.

"Another lesson, another song," huffed Qu'Tkar.

"Did you expect anything less?" asked his father.

"No," Qu'Tkar replied. "But is it wrong to expect more? The Magisters never answer my questions. I ask them about shadows and they sing me another song. It is as if they have something to hide."

"You know how the Drengali people feel about shadows," Qu'Glator replied. "They fear anything that might block the light of the seven stars."

"If their radiance were ever blocked even for an instant, we would surely die," added Qe'Lashar.

"I have heard this a thousand times, Mother," said Qu'Tkar. "But I feel there is more that the Magisters are not telling us."

"Sometimes you need to find the answers for yourself, my son," replied Qu'Glator. "I had altercations with the Magisters when I was your age. My curiosity brought me more trouble than it was worth. But it was this same curiosity that led me to explore the oceans of Drengali. If I had not gone on such excursions, I would never have met your mother."

Qe'Lashar blushed at her husband.

"I understand, Father," replied Qu'Tkar. "The relentless heat of Ebuutan and the sister stars is sometimes more than I can bear."

"Ebuutan provides!" his mother gasped. "Without its warmth and light, and the very seas it provides, where would we be?"

"Sometimes I feel Ebuutan traps us in the very ocean it created," he replied.

"Enough talk of such things, my son," interrupted his father. "We will speak of this later. Now, let us finish our meal in peace."

Qu'Tkar pulled another mollusk from its shell with his spear, ate it, then rose from the table and went to his room: a section of his parents' chamber separated by rows of seaweed that rose vertically from the ocean floor. His father finished the last of his algae salad, then rose from the table and followed him to his room.

"I do not have a song to bring you peace, my son," started Qu'Glator. "But I do have a gift."

Qu'Glator extended a package made of seaweed. Qu'Tkar took it, rummaged inside, and felt a length of giant kelp, green and thick, with strong fibers and numerous sacks running along its length. "You have trained yourself well to travel the above world. This should help you as you explore."

"This is wonderful," Qu'Tkar said as he wrapped the kelp scarf around his neck. He pinched a sack and felt the water stored within discharge into the sea.

"You must be careful," his father urged. "The water stored within the kelp will help sustain you. But in the above world, the heat of Ebuutan and the sister stars is relentless. You will not have the oceans to protect you."

"This will help immensely, Father," said Qu'Tkar. "I plan on leaving for the shoreline while the sisters are low in the sky."

"What are you looking for this time?" asked his father.

Qu'Tkar shook his head as he returned the kelp into the bag. "More than what Ebuutan reveals to us."

"Ebuutan reveals all," replied his father. "The seven stars of Drengali, along with our world, are all that exists. What more do we need?"

"I think the stars blind us," replied Qu'Tkar. "I have been watching their path, and at times they hide behind one another. What if one day they all hid behind Ebuutan while Ebuutan itself was somehow hidden from Drengali?"

"You speak of the darkness," replied Qu'Glator.

"Like the shadows that appear during the replenishing?"

"This goes beyond shadows," said his father. "I know the Magisters would not sing songs about such things to you." With his hand, he parted the seaweed that made up the wall of Qu'Tkar's room and watched his wife tending her garden. "There are songs about this of which even your mother is not aware."

Qu'Glator's gills flared, then he closed his eyes and concentrated. Carefully, and as quietly as possible, he began to sing.

When Drengali falls in a dark time
The world will sow a harvest prime
The history that came to pass
Will nevermore be made to last
The minds of Drengali's people yearn
On a world no longer made to burn
As darkness comes to claim its prize
Liberating blinded eyes
Behold the truth to be proclaimed
History thrown as knowledge gained
Singing chapters of the story
New songs revealed in all its glory

"What is darkness, Father?" asked Qu'Tkar, his eyes wide with fascination.

"It is a concept based in heresy," his father replied. "Some believe there are places that exist free of the light of Ebuutan." He chuckled at the foolishness of the idea. "The light is life. Although the illumination from the seven stars can be harsh, to be without it, even for an instant, would mean certain death."

"A place without light? This is darkness?" asked Qu'Tkar. "But how can such a place be? What does it look like?"

"A place like that does not exist," his father replied. "Look up at the sky, and you see the light of the seven stars is everywhere. Darkness is a fantasy of old fools. A concept contrived by the minds of madmen, best forgotten. Now, take your gift and be off. I would go with you, but my legs have not been strengthened to navigate the above world as well as yours. Besides, someone must keep your mother occupied so she does not worry about you."

Qu'Glator flashed his son a smile, then embraced him. Parting the wall of the room, he swam toward his wife as Qu'Tkar departed with all speed toward the shores of Drengali.

*

The suns loomed overhead, and even in the water he could feel their heat. He broke the surface and saw Ebuutan dominating the sky, with Zeri and Ferius looming overhead. Najar, the blue star that burned the hottest in the sky, as well as the twin yellow stars Phoberus and Felix, were hidden behind Ebuutan.

Qu'Tkar touched the sea floor as he approached the shoreline. He took a full inhale of water, then carefully stepped onto the dry land. His second eyelids lowered as he started inland. He could feel the warm air and the radiance of the stars turning the sea water on his body into vapor. Even with the rays of three stars blocked by Ebuutan, the heat in the above world was stifling. He opened the bag his father had given him and wrapped the seaweed around his head and torso. Immediately he felt relief from the heat that ravaged his moist, smooth skin.

As his eyes adjusted to the dry air and the brilliant light of the suns, Qu'Tkar gazed at his surroundings. The above world of Drengali consisted of massive dunes. He tore off two lengths of kelp and wrapped his feet to keep them from burning when they touched the sand. His feet protected, Qu'Tkar stood up and walked onto the barren land before him. This world was so close to him, but so alien. He felt as if he had somehow been transported to a world other than Drengali. *Another world.* The idea of such a thing intrigued him, but he knew that no other worlds existed because the songs of Drengali told him so.

He looked back at the sea and the safety it provided, then turned and continued onward. As they had been in the past, his legs were shaky at first, but adapted better than during his previous excursions. He walked a short way, peering around at the vastness of the desert before him. He saw nothing but sand. No signs of vegetation like what thrived in the sea. No animals scurried like the fish in the waters near his home.

Nothing.

Qu'Tkar had discovered he could take in the air he needed through the pores of his skin as long as it remained wet. He felt the water pulsing within the sacks of the kelp as he walked. Qu'Tkar had left the ocean, but he had brought enough of it with him to continue onward.

Najak, the hottest of the sister stars, was nowhere to be seen. The twin stars spun around each other as their journey around Ebuutan took them to a lower point in the sky. Sketerus and Zeri were high in the eastern sky, while a sliver of Ferius could be seen sinking past the edge of Drengali. During all his excursions, Qu'Tkar had never seen the stars aligned so, and for a moment, he imagined what it would be like if they had vanished. But he knew they still existed in the vastness of the sky around him because the songs had told him so.

The light of the sister stars is eternal.

He hummed the line from the *Song of the Seven Suns* while he continued forward. The heat and dryness of the air was stifling. He lifted the kelp over his head and burst open a sac. The water ran down his head and covered his body. Rejuvenated, he continued onward.

Qu'Tkar leaned forward and examined the sand. The particles that made up the upper world were free to move about under the slightest breeze. But for now, the air was still. Peering down, he saw imprints, smaller than a droplet, scattered across the sand. Qu'Tkar looked back at the sea, which suddenly seemed so far away. He wondered if any creatures from the ocean had made their way onto the above world as he had done. But the paths didn't reach the sea, and tracing them back toward the dunes, Qu'Tkar could see additional tracks intertwined. At this intersection, he could see the bones and skull of a very small creature left to decay under the scorching suns. He touched the skull with his hand, and felt the dryness of the bone, and noticed the small sockets where eyes should have been. Sections of limbs were scattered about; bones fractured, skin left to bake. Although the Drengali songs would say otherwise, it seemed there were creatures that lived outside the oceans. It also appeared these creatures did not abide by the *Song of Feasting.*

If fin or hand and eyes they share
Their bodies we shall always spare

Maybe the songs were not entirely true.

"Savages," Qu'Tkar concluded. "Little, ignorant savages."

As Qu'Tkar continued onward, he noticed the sky become a mix of red and blue. Ebuutan sank lower in the sky, with the twin yellow stars of Phoberus and Felix chasing it. Of the seven stars that made up the universe, four no longer shined their relentless light on Drengali.

Six-star sisters forever roam
Their dance 'round Ebuutan is flown
Providing with its awesome might
Drengali drenched with endless light

Qu'Tkar continued forward, realizing his pods of water were dwindling in number. In his mind he traced the usage of the pods.

Half to use for the voyage inland.
Half to return to the sea.

He was most diligent in this regard. He knew his life depended on it. Removing the kelp around his head for the briefest moment, he checked the number of pods still remaining, then wrapped it around his head and draped it over his shoulders. With water to spare, he continued onward.

Qu'Tkar followed the footprints across the desert. Fortunately, there was no breeze to wipe away the tracks, and although the small markings darted in several directions, he persisted in tracking them. He squeezed another pod of water to refresh himself, careful not to wash away the tracks. Revived, he increased his pace until the tracks terminated abruptly. He spun around, searching as if the trail had somehow sensed him coming and disappeared. Qu'Tkar dropped to his knees, the sand immediately scorching his skin. Ignoring the pain, he plunged his hands into the sand where the last tracks were discovered, determined to find this creature that lived in the above world.

He was enthralled that the sand, once moved, had no tendency to refill itself like the holes he had dug outside his room of his parents' chamber. The water would return the materials pulled from the sea floor faster than he could empty it, and soon the task became futile. Here in the above world, although small amounts of loose sand ran back into the hole, most of the material stayed where Qu'Tkar had moved it.

He worked at a furious pace, bursting another pod of water onto his hands to keep them from burning. Standing up to pause from the labor, he scanned the sky. Ebuutan was falling toward the horizon in the distance. The sky above turned from blue to red with streaks of purple. Phoberus and Felix, the twin yellow stars, were no longer present. Zeri, the small red star, also hid itself from view, as had Sketerus. All that was left was Ebuutan, and the edge of its massive sphere sank quickly behind the dry, barren landscape of Drengali.

The red sky turned to purple as the light bled out of the sky like blood from a wounded fish under the sea. The white clouds, dominated by the seven stars, asserted themselves in the sky, their billowing forms transformed from the purest white to glowing red as if pulled from Ebuutan itself.

The sky behind the clouds grew less lustrous. It seemed to fall away from Drengali like a piece of kelp torn free from the ocean floor, left to wander aimlessly. To Qu'Tkar, it appeared that the universe had been mortally injured and was about to die, taking Drengali with it.

Fear infected his entire being as the clouds turned a deep grey, their trip through the sky more languorous now that they were no longer bombarded by the relentless fury of the seven suns. Far too quickly for Qu'Tkar to comprehend, the clouds darkened as the sky behind them turned a deeper red, then purple. Finally, as Ebuutan slowly descended behind Drengali, taking the sister stars with it, the sky became absent of all light.

Darkness had overtaken the world of Drengali.

Qu'Tkar was gripped with terror unlike anything he had ever felt before. Bursting several of the pods on the kelp, he dowsed himself in water, as if somehow the remnants of the ocean could sustain him during this dark and dire time. He dropped to his hands and knees and gripped the hot ground with both hands as if without the light of Ebuutan to drive him into the surface, he would float away into the emptiness that was the darkness and fall into its black maelstrom of doom. The ground itself, and his very hands that were plunged into it, soon became invisible to him. The darkness had taken hold in a way he could never have dreamed possible. It had taken his body from him, had taken the land from beneath his feet, and soon, with the absence of the life-giving light of Ebuutan to sustain him, it would soon take his life.

He thought of his father and mother and felt a sudden sense of loneliness. If he were to meet this impending doom, he thought it better to suffer the fate of darkness in the company of his loving family than alone in the midst of the arid and already lifeless desert.

Qu'Tkar hoped his death would be a quick one, free of pain and sorrow. At least he would share his fate with the rest of Drengali.

He waited for the end. The end of his life. The end of everything he knew.

But the end never came. He pulled his hands from the ground and burst several pods above his head. The water washed over his gills and refreshed his skin so he could breathe.

He could still breathe.

Qu'Tkar rose from the ground and lifted his head, peering into the vastness above him. Through the darkness, he perceived a wondrous speckling of lights that filled the sky. He wiped his eyes as if to clear them, but twinkling specks remained. With a sudden tranquility, he gazed up at them in awe. Fear changed to wonder at the vastness that lay before him. He laughed out loud and spread his arms in reverence.

"The light of Ebuutan can also blind us," he called out to the void. For the first time in his life, that light had been lifted. The suns that scorched and burned Drengali were momentarily hidden behind the very world it had created. Qu'Tkar gazed at the majesty of the dark expanse above him, which contained evidence of countless Ebuutans scattered among the vastness. He marveled at the sight of these distant suns, stars yet to be named, and wondered if they contained other worlds like Drengali, with oceans and creatures. He turned to the east as Ebuutan began to rise above the edges of Drengali. Qu'Tkar abandoned the kelp and raced for the safety of the ocean, and as the sky began to brighten, he peered once more at the wonder newly revealed to him, soon to be hidden again.

And the stars sang to him.

Kevin Duarte is a graduate of Roger Williams University. His novel *The Culinary Chronicles of James Dixon - volume 1: Flashpoint* is currently being solicited to agents. His first novel, *Manifest Destiny*, is awaiting a rewrite, and his sci-fi novel *The Copernicus Factor* should be completed and submitted to agents by the end of the year.

PANDEMIC

by Don J. Metivier

Our world spins with grief from a wretched viral event
Unleashed, as the warm tides of Spring begin to appear.
The waves carry us hope, but for just a tentative moment
For, now uncertain times make no one promises here.

Each day the mighty sun shines its life-giving light,
To be obscured below, by sinister shadows of torment.
Where something beyond horror lingers out of sight,
Ready to deliver its fateful curse that hell hath sent!

Gruesome, dark body bags are lined up inside and out.
They await us, as pathogens attack with relentless might.
Invisible and insidious killers, they freely roam about
Making monsters come true, as real as the night.

Separated and spaced apart, we try to avoid the sick and needy.
In homecare and donning masks, we sanitize to ease our worry.
Improvise, as essential store supplies are depleted by the greedy.
As the death toll rises exponentially, bodies can't soon be buried.

Damn this wicked pestilence trying to carry away our future!
Today, many will pray as we seek some safer tomorrow
Where life again is filled with good health and fervor.
Until then, nothing will ease our mounting losses and sorrow.

On, we will forge into these new foreboding days and times,
And with trials and tribulations, good souls will be the cost.
Forever they to rest in survivors' anguished hearts and minds,
Where their spirits and legacies will live on, until all is lost. —

Don J. Metivier is a United States Air Force (Retired) Master Sergeant. He is a member of the Association of Rhode Island Authors, and author of *O Circo: Collective Poetry and Poems from the Mind of a Madman: Passionate Works of Poetry for Modern Times*. He resides in New Hampshire.

NEIGHBORS

by Patricia Cousineau

It had been a dreary wet week. My friends and I were thinking about Googling blueprints for an ark, but the rain finally stopped last evening. The morning dawned bright and dry, and I planned to head to the supermarket for salad dressing and crusty bread to go with the garden bounty that my neighbor had brought to me. Mrs. Norma Jean Phipps, who was turning 80 today, had the best garden in town. Her vegetables were rivalled by none. She lived alone, but her youngest son, Ronnie, had devoted many hours to tending her garden, often working late into the night after he finished his shift at the local meat-packing plant.

As I left the house, the day seemed ordinary enough: car in the driveway, newspaper on the lawn, old Mrs. Phipps running naked through the shrubbery, the cat waiting to come in...old Mrs. Phipps running naked? No. That was not an ordinary sight. It was her birthday, but I didn't expect to see her in her birthday suit. She was screaming as she ran.

"The cat! The cat!" she yelled as she rounded the corner of the house and headed into Mr. Beach's backyard. I didn't know what was happening with the cat, but Mr. Beach had better have his heart medication handy.

My cat, Shilo, gazed up at me with a look that said, "I am waiting to get inside and I have no knowledge of what all this fuss is about. Nor do I care."

I opened the door and she quickly scooted down the hallway in the direction of her food dish. I closed the door and walked across the lawn, which was still damp from the recent rains. I headed for Mrs. Phipps' open front door. Maybe I would discover what had sent her on her naked marathon.

I had not been in her house in some time. We were the kind of neighbors who did most of our socializing over the shrubbery and the wild roses that divided our back yards. We shared plant cuttings and weather chatter. She would pull the latest grandchild photo out of her gardening apron pocket, and I would keep her posted on my latest performances at the local community theater. I had driven her to the supermarket a few times when her son was unavailable, and I had helped carry her groceries inside.

As I entered the living room, I saw that the grandchildren photos had reproduced astronomically, now covering every available table-top, as well as the mantel over the fireplace. The sun shone in the windows through lace curtains, and everything was neat, tidy, and in its place. Her big orange tabby George, however, was disheveled and quite muddy, perched on an antique brocade chair and playing with something that looked like it had once been alive. Could a chewed-up mouse have driven Mrs. Phipps to abandon all modesty and run out of the house? I moved closer to the chair to get a better look at George's plaything. Oh, my God! No wonder Mrs. Phipps had fled in such a hurry.

Rushing through the kitchen, I pulled my phone out of my pocket and dialed 911. This was a situation that I did not want to tackle alone. The kitchen held no clues. It was as neat and tidy as the living room had been: breakfast dishes washed and drained, curtains opened to welcome the glorious sunshine.

The door to the bathroom was ajar. The wet shower and a large green bath towel draped over the closed toilet lid suggested what Mrs. Phipps might have been doing when George entered with his catch of the day.

I opened the back door and heard the first wail of sirens. Beyond, the yard was a lush green. The dirt in the garden at the far end of the yard had formed a slight crust from the sun. The week's rain had softened it and now it was drying out. The vegetables seemed to be thriving. I looked around the yard as I waited for the police to arrive. Mrs. Phipps hesitantly rounded the corner of her garage, wrapped in a plaid fringed couch throw. It wasn't her best color, but it covered the necessary areas. Mr. Beach trailed behind.

"Sophie," she called. "Did you see what George had?" she asked with a quiver in her voice.

"Yes, I did, and I've called the police. They should be here any minute."

She and Mr. Beach crossed into the yard by the rose bushes and came to stand beside me.

"I was so frightened when I saw it in George's mouth that I just ran. I guess I forgot that I was not dressed. I feel like such a fool."

"Don't be silly. Anyone would be shocked and scared by such a sight. I'm glad that Mr. Beach came to your rescue."

Sheepish grins covered their faces.

I noticed a spot in the far corner of the garden, between the row of lettuce and the row of carrots, where the muddy ground was disturbed. It looked like a sizeable hole had been dug.

"It looks like something happened in the garden," I said.

Followed by my companions, I went in for a closer look. I soon discovered the cache of treasure that George had unearthed poking up from the turned earth. I heard someone screaming from far off. As I fell to the ground and the light began to fade, I realized the voice sounded like mine.

When I came to, I was lying on the cushions of Mrs. Phipps' lavender chaise lounge. Mr. Beach was fanning me with an AARP magazine. The back yard was a beehive of activity. Police uniforms and yellow crime scene tape were the new garden decorations and Mrs. Phipps was sitting in a police cruiser in the driveway. A man in a suit was talking earnestly with her and she was struggling to hold back tears.

"What is happening, Mr. Beach? I remember a hand, a hand coming up out of the garden, a hand with a missing finger, and ...oh, my God, tell me there wasn't a body in the garden."

"I'm afraid there was, and not just one by the looks of it. They're still digging, and they seem to think the garden is a very populated graveyard."

"But Ronnie was just tilling the soil a few days ago. Surely he would have come across...Oh, no. Do they think that Ronnie...? No, it can't be. He's such a good son, a nice quiet man, shy and polite."

"It looks like he may also be one of the most wanted serial killers in this part of the country. The police have gone to arrest him."

"Poor Mrs. Phipps. What a shock for her. To think he may have been doing this for years and no one ever suspected. And the vegetables..." At this thought I gagged and had to sit up and put my head between my knees to calm myself.

"They're closing the meat-packing plant until they can test samples of the products," added Mr. Beach.

That thought was enough to propel me out of the chaise and in the direction of my own house and, perhaps, a return to some sanity.

"I don't want to hear any more right now, Mr. Beach. Give my best to Mrs. Phipps. This has been one hell of a birthday surprise. Tell the police they can come and talk with me in my house when they're ready. I need to get away from this darkness."

George was sitting on my front steps, licking his paws, when I crossed the lawn. It seemed like days since I had left my house. In reality, it was just hours ago.

"Go home, you foul animal, and take that finger to the cops. You can't play with Shilo for a very long time."

I opened my door and entered my cluttered but homey living room, leaving the madness behind me in Mrs. Phipps' yard. I might never leave here again. I dropped onto the sofa and closed my eyes, but that brought back visions of the hand with four fingers in the garden. I opened my eyes and my gaze wandered to the kitchen counter, just visible through the archway in my living room. There sat the carrots and lettuce that Mrs. Phipps had brought me last evening. I sighed. I don't think I'll be having a salad for lunch today.

Patricia Cousineau has worked for over 40 years in early childhood education. She published her first children's book in 2022 and her second is on its way. Her desire has always been to write a novel and she is working on that as well. Being included in this anthology is an honor.

THE WIDOW BARRETT

by Yvette Nachmias-Baeu

A spinster? Is she that now? No, that's not right. She's been married twice, raised a son, divorced once and is now a widow. That's what she is — a widow. She is the widow Barrett.

The house is quiet except for the refrigerator's loud humming motor. Surprisingly, she never hears it until the motor stops, creating an eerie silence.

Feeling creaky this morning, she gets up, leans against the armoire her husband made just before he died. Stretching out her calves, before pulling on a sweatshirt and yoga pants, she gingerly walks down the stairs to where the cats demand their first meal of the day. Spring is coming and the clocks have skipped forward to Daylight Savings Time, bidding Eastern Daily Time goodbye till next fall. She notices with delight that she managed to sleep later than her usual six hours, and now it's light outside. She never liked waking up in the dark. The sun is shining through the windows and all the dust she thought was vacuumed away yesterday is clearly visible. Ignoring her cats' insistent meowing, she steps out onto the porch, her feet still bare. The deck is wet from last night's rainfall. The bird feeder is empty. The sun is well over the horizon. She is surprised and excited when she hears the loud honking cackle of geese flying overhead, returning from their southern habitat, noisily splashing down on the surface of the pond. They are the first sign of spring. Looking over at the small bed of bulbs she planted last fall, she calls out a happy hello, seeing the green shoots bursting out of the ground. Katherine Barrett takes a deep breath and feels surer, knowing she will be okay. She's gotten through another winter, but then she knows a big snowstorm is expected in a day or two. March is like that.

Back inside, she opens a can of food for her two still-unfriendly cats, walks outside again, this time with shoes, to fill the bird feeder. The birds swoop down from their perches on the surrounding tree branches, singing and chirping as they crowd around the feeder. It is the small things — these perfect moments that allow Katherine to celebrate her life. I'm alright, she thinks, and turns her attention to the dreary remnants of winter's debris scattered over the backyard. What to do, she wonders, about making this backyard look better. How should she deal with all the trouble spots? Maybe a row of boxwood over to the right side of her house. She could make Christmas wreaths out of their succulent foliage and the shrubs will stay green year-round. Invigorated by the thought of a new project, she rushes inside to find paper and pencil, puts on the coffee, and goes back outside, enthusiastically drawing out what she hopes to see at long last—a fine-looking yard. What is perfectly clear is that a husband is no longer part of her life. She has to admit that with advancing age comes the end of certain adventures. She wonders if she is still young enough and strong enough to be completely independent. She must learn to take better care of herself, and conduct life in a different way.

It is time to ignore her age and the thought that she might need someone to help carry the heavy bags of mulch and topsoil and dig the holes for the new shrubs. Obstinately, she plans to put up the window screens and change the burned-out lightbulbs, even though that requires a ladder. And the smoke alarm, installed high on the wall, needs new batteries. It's been chirping for a week. She stubbornly refuses to accept the possibility that she cannot do these things herself. She is determined to manage.

The question she keeps asking herself is what will the next five years look like? Five more years is all the time she is willing to give herself. After that, she figures she will have to get creative and find a way to end her life. It's been a thought that has been circling around her mind for quite some time. She has a desperate need to get out, while she is still able to walk on her own, while she still knows her own name and recognizes her son. But five years isn't a lot of time. She reminds herself how quickly the last five years have gone by since her husband passed away. She has put off thinking about so many things. Her family, her finances, what happens if she isn't able to drive. Who will take care of her cats once she is gone? But these thoughts mostly play in the back of her mind, and only alarm her when they pop up uninvited. And her son. Who exactly is he these days? He hasn't really confided in her for a number of years. Not really. Grown sons don't let their mothers know much about themselves. Where, in fact, are all the people she once knew? Her friends and peers. Most of them have died. Their joint history and accomplishments are almost forgotten now. The memories of them are only alive and carried by the few that will soon join them. Then it will be as if they were never here at all. She's put off thinking about all these things, because procrastination is one of her finer attributes, or so she contends.

Aside from going to the grocery store, the post office, and the drug store, spending an hour at the gym each day, taking a long walk, or having lunch with a friend, there is not much else that occupies her days. Yes, these years have given her more time to read and she is sure she has watched every movie ever made. She no longer takes off for a weekend, traveling to destinations she used to choose at random or go to political rallies or join in community events. It gets harder and harder to emotionally leave her house.

Thinking about where to plant ground cover and a hedgerow temporarily makes her happy. She can put off thinking about all the inconvenient things that might beset her. She has plenty of time to work on her gardening plan. Lots of time. But then again, time may be in short supply.

As spring warms up the days and nights, she begins her project. She finds ingenious ways to move the 50-pound bags of topsoil and mulch using her wheelbarrow. She's set up the garden hose, and before the boxwoods are delivered, she digs and prepares fourteen holes to accept them. Never mind that it takes her three days to dig them all and another four to plant the very last shrub. They will grow and be here long after she is gone. The little garden is pushing up all the perennials she planted a few seasons back, and the annuals she got from her favorite nursery will fill in the empty spaces. The garden will be colorful all summer long. When the last plant is in the ground, she steps back and surveys her work, satisfied that she did it all by herself.

Yet something nags at her. The same old question. "Is this it? Is this my third act?" Recalling that after her husband died, she spent a lot of time thinking of ways to change her life so she wouldn't miss him so much. She thought of doing volunteer work in Utah, at an animal sanctuary. She thought about a lot of things, but in the end didn't do any of them. She is running out of time. This may be her last chance.

Doing some research and making a number of calls, she dares to consider something quite different than anything she has done before. It's time that her last act be an adventure, aging or not. Deciding, almost cavalierly, to do something bold, knowing it might dramatically alter her life or maybe even shorten it. She is not entirely sure she can do it, but she knows she has to try.

In researching her options, she decides to volunteer for a project in Barundi, Africa, where two-thirds of its population is infected with HIV. Having once been a nurse, this seems the most dramatic choice. She is filled with a blissful sense of purpose. Her final act on this earth will confront at least one major challenge. Helping some people, or even only one person out of their misery will be enough and so she sets out doggedly making all the necessary preparations, to the consternation of her son, who insists she is mad.

On her first day, the sweltering heat sucks up all her energy. It is so hot she feels she can't breathe. She has to get used to this climate and the conditions she lives in. At first, the sweat pouring off her and the fatigue renders her practically immobile. She worries that her fellow volunteers will report her as unfit. There are days she thinks she's made a huge mistake and will have to forfeit her desire to be of service. Each long day drags on. She hopes she will make it to the next. Carrying on the struggle, one day at a time, she is determined to grow accustomed to her surroundings; she needs to master the hot humid days and the fear and discomfort that are all part of her life now. The washroom and toilets are outdoor communal sheds, her bed a canvas cot. Besides the uncomfortable living quarters shared with three others, there is the everyday nightmare she observes: tending to the endless line of people, emaciated, sick, and dying. The loaded rifle given to her is stowed away under her cot, and a daily reminder of the threat from the marauding tribes that often attempt to disrupt the camp in this mostly French outpost.

Her French is poor but over time she begins to understand her fellow volunteers and feels her courage building and her strength and energy increasing. The work of teaching disease and HIV prevention goes on daily. Treating the sick and dying infiltrates every one of her senses and every other minute of her waking day. She can't get used to the fact that most of the people she sees have no chance of getting better. Yet she lives with the hope that some will and that a new generation will not only survive, but thrive. Still, the current problems facing these people are monumental and there are times she fears they may not have the chance to live the lives their ancestors crafted. She stakes her hopes on the squadron of young people that are teaching these people new farming techniques, proper sanitary practices, and birth control. One of the ways she copes with the daily parade of the dying is to care about them, but she avoids getting too close to anyone for fear she won't have the will to continue.

The widow Barrett, "Katie" as she is called here, spends over a year in Africa. Her skin brown from the almost constant sun, and stronger than she has felt in years, she is sent home once to take a break, as everyone must, but returns after a few months' respite. Katie is happy to return, feeling more prepared than before, though her hair has turned a cottony white.

After another year, she is leaving Africa again, this time for good. Sad to leave the work still not done, she returns home by way of Paris. She spends a few weeks revisiting every place she's ever been, figuring she will not be back again.

Depositing herself in her silent home, with the cats returned from their foster home and unfriendlier than ever for having been left behind, she fears she will fall back into the same old patterns: groceries, drug store, the gym. But this time she is fortified by the knowledge that she's been useful. She's done something with her waning years. She has participated in her third and final act.

Opening her desk calendar, she sees the red marking she made five years ago, signifying that this would be the year. Hemlock or laughing gas, she wonders. Sleeping pills and champagne, perhaps.

As she ponders the most effective method for her demise, a stray dog wanders into her yard. He is all bones and ticks. His eyes are sadder than the whole world. He is too weak to bark, and walks up to her back door, flopping down like a rag doll. She opens the door cautiously and talks to him in a soft whisper. He doesn't seem to want to go anywhere. Leaving him on the porch, she returns with water and then, into another bowl, she spoons out major scraps from last night's dinner. He empties the bowl of water and hungrily licks the food bowl clean. Painstakingly she removes all the ticks she can find with the dog comb she kept even though her beloved Labrador, Odin, died many years ago. Her new charge sits patiently, accepting her attention.

Coaxing him into her bathtub, which requires some effort, he stands limply, allowing her to wash him clean. As he dries in the sun, she brushes him till his mangy coat begins to take on a bit of shine. It seems clear he has adopted her. Katherine feels the responsibility of her new charge, brings him to the veterinarian to make sure he is going to be alright.

Weeks have gone by since he showed up at her back door. He is livelier now and gaining weight. It was hard to tell at first but now he is showing signs of having lots of shepherd in his mongrel mix. They both like taking long walks together in the neighboring woods and he doesn't even mind the leash. She lets him run free when they are far from the busy road. He bounds off ahead of her, but comes running back from time to time to make sure she is still there.

It is another chilly, early spring night. She's lived through so many spring days. She makes a fire and sits comfortably reading in her favorite armchair. The stray dog, she has named Argos, is sleeping peacefully at her feet. Every once in a while, she leans down and gently pats his big furry head. The widow Barrett, Katie, breathes in and with a deep exhale seems content to give herself a bit more time.

Yvette Nachmias-Baeu is the author of the award-winning *A Reluctant Life,* a memoir about the process of grief; *Clara at Sixty,* the fictionalized sequel; and *Best Friends,* a chronicle of a friendship. Her latest, *Ledicia's Key,* follows a family through six centuries. She lives and writes at the edge of a waterfall.

MARATHON

by Jack Nolan

Annie O'Meara Conover fondly watched as the great love of her mature life pulled all the raisins out of his cereal with his fingertips, gently setting each on his placemat until he could find no more hiding under the milk. While she read to him from The Miami Herald, he ate all his cereal, smashed his rye toast into the bottom of the empty bowl with his spoon and cleared his place by pushing everything into the center of the table, leaving nothing on the plastic mat before him but scattered raisins.

When she read, "Atlanta made it three straight, beating the Pirates six to four in a game that was close until the ninth," he told her firmly, "You already read that."

RATS !! rats in the galley, boys. crud in the meal.. wage war best we can. fish 'em out. out. with our. with our. by hand. it's sick bay sure. sick boys to sick bay. sick boys. eat black crud will do you in. Oh-Oh. clear decks for action. haven't got all day for chow. put her away, boys. 'at's it. good job. swab out those bowls, boys. stand fast. stand ready for inspection. bosin. go go. attention all hands. captain speaking. clear decks for action. battle stations! battle stations! is she one of ours? hold steady. steady. take aim. wait for it. can't find it. steady. tell her! tell her! trouble ahead! game's afoot. close quarters! one...two...steady... fire one! fire two! KaBoom! KaBoom! got her! she didn't see that comin'. told her. ha! captain! she's coming

She thought about agreeing for a moment but chose the truth. "No, honcy," she said.

"Yes, deeear," he growled. "You read that!"

"Okay, that's it, I'm not reading to you," she told him. She put down the newspaper and looked out at a pelican preening itself. He stared at his reflection. She brought him a cup of lukewarm coffee and his red notebook. When the doorbell rang, she called out from the kitchen, "Aren't you going to get that? Very well, then. I will." It amused her to play such games, treating misfortune with the salve of comedy.

The woman holding her photo I.D. card against the screen was uncommonly pretty—generous features with dark eyes, wearing a full dress of bright colors that set off her olive skin. "Mrs. Conover, I'm Maria Acosta, nurse's aide with the county?" she said, making it sound like a question.

"Yes, do please come in." Annie fished a ring of keys out and began counting through them. "I've had locks installed, you know, or he is prone to wander off. We have

about! close quarters! fire! fire! fire! KaBoom! KaBoom! put some lead into her that time, cap'n! she's running up the flag. got her good. at'll hold 'er. put that one across her brow.

pirates be damned matey. that'll hold her. squeeeze her. tell her that you neeed her. nuts'n butter pound dog. crockin' alla time. nuts'n butter pound dog. crockin' alla time. man at table. staring this way. know him? stare back. she with him? her back to me. know her? hi glaaass. that'a just a lie. hi glaaass. that'a just a lie. she's one of our own, boys. know him? sure. he's mark twin. mean tamper. don't stare. start a ruckus. ignore 'em both. she up and left him. serves him right. the lists! good! here we go. find it. find it. sssshh! where is she? lost for good. twin alone. wave to him. hello. hi. waves back. a friend in need. find it now. find it. here! Birthday. 1. Guitar. 2. Fish Food. 3. Promise. now now. don't spill it. clear decks for action, boys. steady as she goes. set her down easy. up now. twin up now. he is standing. bye. wave. waves back. bye now. step lively, lads. quick. chair down. sssshh! damn! set it aside. careful like. over a canal in the back and we don't want him falling in, even though he's always been a good swimmer and I suppose he still could if he had to...here it is...this is the right one."

"How many in the family, then?"

"Pardon?"

"You said 'we don't want him falling in.'"

"Oh, there's just the two of us, him and me. That's the 'we' I guess, although I don't think he'd mind falling in, really. But I would, most days."

"So you're able to manage on your own?"

"Yes, well, so far. Here, watch the step up. There are 26-hour days now and again, but he sleeps pretty well most nights. I sleep when he does and, well, so far so good. But we're at that point now where going shopping is about impossible so I'm very glad you're here because it's his birthday, he knows it's his birthday, well, sometimes he knows it but he never remembered mine so now that he's forgetting his own that's turn-about and fair play. Let me get you a cup of coffee. We can sit

here. list now. 1. Guitar. good. stay with it. steady as she goes. there she is. in doorway. talking to herself. perfect!! go go go go.

quiet now. safe! safe! slip into dark. dark. easy. stay with it. steady. where is it? quiet please. easy. here it is. easy as she goes. place it down. quiet please. 1. Guitar. got it. got it. oh god. oh god. what's 2? get it. what's 2? get it. 2 is. 2 is.2 is. 2 is. number 1 is Guitar. number 2 is. 2 is. get it. on list. here. hide. find it. hang on dear life

bitch! goddamned bitch! hang on! find it! number 1. Guitar. 2 is. 2 is. 2 is. Again like we did last summer. 2 is. 2 is.2 is. 2 is.2 is. 2 is.2 is. we did last yeeear! tump. tump. at ease, men. as you were. stay with the mission. keep together. accomplish the missing. straighten those lines! attennnnn-hut! sound off by the numbers! yes sir! seaman recruit. seaman apprentice. seaman. petty officer third class. petty officer second class. petty officer first class. chief petty officer. senior chief petty officer. master chief petty officer. master chief petty officer of the navy. ankle-bone shinbone thighbone hipbone. ha! wipe that smile off'n your face, boy. yes sir. company commander on the lanai and get introduced to...now where is he?!"

Patrick's coffee cup was in the center of his plastic mat, full and encircled by raisins, and his chair was pushed into the far corner of the sun-filled porch, but he had gone. Annie quickly assured herself that the back door was still locked, then they went toward the rear of the house, checking bedrooms, bathrooms, and closets. They found him crashing around in the dark garage. Annie switched on the garage light and there Patrick stood, looking startled, arms wrapped around his black guitar case.

"Fish food," he said.

"Birthday, you mean?" Annie guessed.

"Yes! Birthday!"

"Okay, well then, are you all right? This is Maria, my dear. She is here to help us do our shopping for your birthday. Come inside now."

ordered you to chow down and suit up. yes sir. pirates expected any minute. look at you!

a disgrace! sir. permission to speak sir! denied! let's get one thing straight! what's that sir? number 1. Guitar. hit it! manger baby....my manger baby ooohooo i love you. ooohoo i do. there they are. not lost. just misplaced. they're right on top of your head, stupid. heads up. feet apart. soldiers together. eyes shut. mouth open. now try to dance that way. arms around girl. 1-2-3. 1-2-3. 1-2-3. come here often? ok break it up. attennnn-hut! abooouuut-hace!! oh god oh god. they got us! two left feet. she tried to lead. her fault. they lit us up out here! just met. she's not my date! never saw her before in my life! we have a birthday surprise.

who said that? yes! ha! front and center, swabbie! way to go! 2 is FISH FOOD! that's it all right! yes! and you too! good girl! Birthday! we're all here. all present and accounted for, sir! sound off by the numbers! 1. Guitar. 2. Fish Food. 3 is. 3 is. 3 is. birthday! no. birthday! no, sir. 2 is Fish Food.

3 is PROMISE! yes! all present and accounted for, sir. ship-shape! ready to shove off! give the order!

Forty minutes later, they were on their way to Marathon, thirty miles of island-hopping through the lush paradise of the Keys on the roads and causeways of Route 1. Annie used Patrick's birthday as an excuse to extend routine shopping into a longer journey away from the house, a holiday from the confinements imposed by his illness. And it was a crisp, beautiful morning with fast-moving clouds riding warm gusts over swaths of the ocean's purple, green, and blue, a playground for pelicans, gulls, egrets, herons, and all of it churning in a sun-blessed dance of life. Annie felt the intensity of spirit that is the perverse gift of a terminal illness in one you love. Life was so fleeting, tenuous, precious beyond comprehension, she wondered how anyone could possibly take any of it for granted, how she herself could have, ever. But there would be time for survivor's guilt later. Now, they were together, making a trip to Marathon on this glorious day in Eden.

Maria too made Annie happy. After they had exhausted the sad business at hand, management strategies for an ultimately unmanageable disease, Maria talked about her own family, which was extensive and full of eccentricities that appealed to Annie's sense of the absurd. Maria rambled on merrily while Patrick sat in silence beside her on the back seat of the van, arms wrapped around his guitar case. They had badgered him into changing his shoes and visiting the bathroom, but nothing could persuade him to leave his guitar at home. So, he cradled it in his lap now like some oversized teddy bear. "He played in a rock band years ago," Annie had said, "but this just isn't like him" and she laughed because, of course, it wasn't like anyone. People who get lost in their minds are in a league of their own when it comes to eccentricity and if you didn't find it funny, you could only weep.

Sometimes, with Maria chattering behind her, Annie would look into the rearview mirror and make eye contact with Patrick. Instead of the furtive eyes that were one mark of his suffering, she caught him gazing calmly into the mirror, directly into her eyes. Having to watch the road, it was now her turn to be furtive while his eyes held steadily on the mirror. She now endured for the sake of those little moments when she was certain that he was still in there—frightened, angry, snared by confusion but his real self nonetheless, that person who could still look out at her, recognize her, and remember.

"I have to go!" he barked out, suddenly agitated.

Maria put both her hands on his arm to try to get his attention and almost shouted at him, "To the bathroom? Mr. Conover, to the bathroom?"

"I have to go!"

To Annie she said, "You know, it's really time for you to think about adult diapers."

"Not yet." Annie was firm. "He's been fine. It isn't time."

"Time!" Patrick agreed and Annie was amused that he was in context, making this off-the-wall response to what was being said around him.

"There's a convenience store just before Seven Mile Bridge, Maria. We'll pop in there and make sure he's okay before the last long stretch into Marathon."

Annie parked on the gravel driveway, and they spent some time getting Patrick unbelted and out of the van, but without any success at parting him from his beloved guitar case. When challenged for it, he hugged it with such strength that Annie worried he might damage the classic Martin itself, which was delicate and no inexpensive toy. So, they entered the store like ants clinging to a grub, arms linked around each other and the black music case. The clerk was visibly startled by the odd sight of this conglomerate lunging toward him, so Annie told him, "Yes...good morning. We are having one of life's little awkward moments and need to use your bathroom, please."

"It's not for the public but okay. All the way in the back, behind the freezer." He pointed the way and, not sure what was going on, he called out, "Only one at a time in there...right?"

"Gotcha!" Annie assured him as they stumbled down the narrow aisle, knocking some cans to the floor. To Patrick she said, "I promise I will stay right here with your guitar, stand right here and hold it for you until you're done in there." And he responded, "Promise!" five or six times but still would not loosen his fierce grip on the instrument.

Maria checked the interior of the toilet. "It's all clear," she said, "Not all that clean but there's no one using it."

While they waited, Maria continued to argue that a diaper regime was best for him. "It'd make things easier on you both, once he's used to it."

"Look, you see how strong he is...and let me show you something." Annie brought the red spiral notebook from her purse. "These are his lists, things he wants to remember and get done, and while he doesn't make the connections you and I would, he does have a certain order of his own. Here, look, he has four or five different..."

A large man in a blue uniform backed a hand-truck stacked with cases of soda up the back steps and into the store through the delivery door. The women stepped aside to let him pass while they continued to talk, so neither was in a position to see the screen door open and shut behind him.

"...Sorry, yes, four or five different lists we worked on together for his birthday and he always says he wants fish, over a couple weeks' time. Whenever 'birthday' comes up, he says, 'fish' and I promise to get him fish and that makes him happy. So, I guess he really has his heart set on some kind of aquarium. He was in the navy for twelve years, but he's never shown any interest in fish before, so I think he has some firm ideas that may not be logical to us but that connect for him and show he does indeed think about things from day to day that must be important to him."

*

On the rough lumber of Bridge Point Pier, Bobby Mills and Chuck Munson had taken all their gear out of the boat and had just popped the caps off their third beer of the day. Mills, perched on the cooler, gave a tug to the loose shirttail of his partner and pointed the neck of his bottle toward dry land. "What the hell do you make of that?" he drawled.

The spindly figure of an old man with a crown of white hair, arms wrapped around a black instrument case, stumbled down the neck of the pier toward them. He had a stricken, wild-eyed expression and a child's unsteady gait, which made a comic impression on Bobby Mills, who stood and put both arms out across the stranger's path, saying, "Whoa there, buddy! You don't want to tumble into the water, you better slow down."

The man looked at Mills' sunburned arm, as though it were a disembodied thing, and then beyond to the horizon and said only, "Promise." He shifted from foot to foot, as agitated as he was distracted.

"Yeah, I promise. You must be with the band, right?" The fishermen exchanged glances and Munson laughed, making a discreet gesture, his finger to his head.

"Promise..."

"Tell you what. My partner here is gonna see if he can find your people. Right, Chuck? And you can play me a little something here while he goes to look for them. That okay with you, buddy?"

Munson moved up the pier, toward the busy convenience store at the top of the rise, while Mills put a hand on the bony shoulder of the old man and coaxed him to let go of the case. Bobby thought he had never seen such a pathetic soul—lost, wandering eyes and a down-turned mouth that could only mutter, "Promise...promise." The old guy gradually relinquished his grip on the case and let Mills lay it on the planks of the pier.

"Now I'll just sit over here and sip my brew, okay? And you go right ahead and play me a little something. Anything you know will be just fine." Mills helped him out by flipping the three catches on the hard case before settling onto the ice chest. He took a pull on his cold beer and was surprised when he looked up to see the old man calm and gazing intently back at him with a look of sane determination.

"Yes, sir," he said to Mills in a quiet, low voice. "I volunteer." He pulled himself erect and saluted with military precision, feet together, then quickly knelt to the guitar case. He flipped the lid back and pulled a shiny, silver revolver with a pearl handle out of the plush, red velvet lining. As soon as he saw what it was, Mills threw his half-empty beer at the old man, aiming for his head. But it missed and both men watched the bottle skip along the decking of the pier, scattering suds in all directions, then roll across the planks toward a petite woman who was running toward them, carrying high heels in her hands. "Don't hurt him," she called out as she came. "I'll take care of him!"

She slowed to a walk as she neared and said quietly, "It's all right, Patrick. I'm here now, come to take you shopping." As she talked, he pointed the revolver at her, not aiming but apparently unconscious of having it and she took no notice of it.

"You really gave us a scare," she said to him, matter-of-factly pulling the gun from his hand, "running away like you did. Did you want to come down here and feed the fishes? Is that what you wanted?" and she smiled as she dropped the weapon into the water with a splash. "Well, let's find them something besides you."

Bobby Mills heard her say to him as she led him away by the arm, "I really love you, you know. You and I just have to see things through all the way to the end."

bar fight! hey...who started this ruckus? you? no sir! he started it. shore patrol is going to come and haul you all to the brig. hold fire boys, she's one of ours. Patrick? not Patrick but something like it. you belong to my heart...... mi corazon! have to carry our shoes here? no one told me. got mine on. such a sweet face on this one. one of our people, come for me to take me to the gig. haul us to the brig. one last gig will be had by all. did you all have a good time tonight? we played our best for you but now sure patrol has come to take us by the hand. no, ma'am, I never fed the fishes. but I promise on my birthday. But not yet. if I can keep the band together. one last solo. she wants me to come with her. first, we have to...have to find Annie.

Jack Nolan enlisted in Army Intelligence in 1967, serving as a civilian-cover spy working with Vietnamese counterparts, where he made a handful of life-long friends. The story of those friendships is at the heart of his comic novels, *Vietnam Remix* and *There Comes a Time*, available, with a guide, at vietnam.remix.1968@ gmail.com.

GARDEN

by Deborah L. Halliday

The furry worms that drop from fruited tree,
When storms arise that rip and shake their ripe
Wet hatchery, find homes among debris
Well suited to their purpose; and a type
Receptive to their charms, incognizant
As on their head one lands and burrows there
To spin its sticky dark entanglement,
Becomes a breeding ground, perhaps aware
When of a night, one crawls into an ear,
Where nursed by careless mind's inconstancy,
It lies, and lies, 'til lies to filth adhere
And make a nest of dank apostasy,
That grows again the furry creatures foul
That drop, and drop, and drop from open mouths.—

Deborah L Halliday began writing sonnets for fun and challenge in 2018 and since then has written over 160. Her sonnets have appeared in the 2021 and 2022 ARIA anthologies, in *Rhode Island Bards 2022, The Bridge* newspaper, and on various websites including gaspee.org and usnamemorialhall.org. Writing continues!

DARKNESS WITHIN

by Paul Lonardo

Paula was sitting at the kitchen table in front of her laptop when Dominic walked into the room. She was cradling a steaming coffee mug with both hands to keep them warm. It was the cup that Christina had given her last Mother's Day, proclaiming her WORLD'S GREATEST MOM.

"Didn't you go to college with an Ethan Palmer?" she asked before he could get out a 'good morning.'

Hearing that name out of the blue sent a shiver down his spine.

"Yeah, Ethan Palmer was the name of my roommate my freshman year," he said as he reached for the pot of freshly brewed coffee.

"Does he live in Glens Falls, New York?" Paula asked.

"I don't know." Dominic removed the carafe from the machine and poured himself a cup of coffee. "Why?"

"He slaughtered his entire family," she said matter-of-factly.

Dominic's hands shook and coffee dribbled over the sides of his cup. He quickly set the mug down on the counter and looked up at his wife. "What?" His voice was edged with terror as he walked over to her, drying his hands on a paper towel.

"Right here." She angled the computer screen toward him. "Glens Falls man massacres family as they sleep," she read the headline.

Dominic enlarged the screen so he could read it without his glasses.

The article was reprinted from the Glens Falls Chronicle, the by-line credited to Jared Wieland and dated yesterday.

A Glens Falls man, Ethan Palmer, 42, was charged with the murder of his family. His wife, Brooke, 38, and the married couple's two children, Glenn, 12, and Avery, 8, were killed as they slept in their beds last night according to the Glens Falls Police Department. Details of the incident are being withheld pending further investigation, but an unnamed source close to the story revealed that the bodies were so savagely ripped apart in the brutal attack that they were rendered unrecognizable, requiring dental records to positively identify the victims. Palmer, visibly distraught and shaken by the incident, proclaimed his innocence, telling reporters that he did not commit this atrocity, insisting that an evil entity was responsible for the massacre.

Dominic scrolled down to continue the article, but the browser went to the next story about a missing Omaha teenager.

"That's it?" he said, looking at his wife with a blank expression and eyes that seemed to pass right through her.

"You think that's the same guy you knew?" Paula asked, taking a sip of her coffee.

Dominic felt a keen instinct to leave it alone and disregard what he'd just read, but he couldn't. He wasn't the type that harbored a fascination for the macabre and all things ghoulish the way his wife did, but he was overcome by a hot flashpoint of shame and guilt, as if he had been responsible in some way for this horrific human tragedy.

"Probably not," he finally responded as he turned back to wipe down the counter.

"I remember you mentioning that he was a little off," Paula said, obliterating any possibility Dominic had of dismissing the news story without further exploration.

"He was peculiar, all right," he conceded.

"In what way?"

Dominic hesitated. There was no way to describe it without going into detail. "Well, he had this weird obsession about keeping the lights on when he slept," he began. "He had some of those flashlights that mechanics use, that you can twist around things. He always had at least one wrapped around his headboard in case his bedside lamp went out."

Paula's jaw dropped and her eyes widened in surprised amusement. "Oh, my God, he was afraid of the dark."

"Lots of people are afraid of the dark," Dominic said, his voice rising. "That doesn't make someone a psychotic murderer. Christina jumped in our bed just last night and insisted we leave a light on."

"She's four," Paula told him. "And in preschool, not college." She didn't know why Dominic was defending the guy. "It's probably not the same Ethan Palmer, but wouldn't that be something if it was," she said with a lift of her eyebrows.

"What do you mean?" Dominic asked.

"Well, it's not like he's Ted Bundy or Jeffrey Dahmer, but you could have been sharing a room with someone that you had no idea was capable of killing another human being. Not many people can say that."

"I guess not," Dominic said absently.

"So, what do you think this guy, whoever he is, meant when he said that an *evil entity* was responsible for the killing?"

Dominic's arm jerked suddenly as he was stirring the cream and sugar into his coffee. He knocked over the cup, spilling coffee across the countertop and soaking the front of his pants.

"Shit!" he shouted. "Now I have to change my pants."

"I'll get that," Paula said, getting up. "Go get changed."

"Sorry, hon." Dominic averted his eyes as she cleaned the countertop.

"Don't worry about it. Christina's always spilling or dropping something. I can make you a coffee to go, with a spill-proof lid."

"No, that's okay. I'll stop for one. Thanks anyway. I'll see you tonight."

"I won't be home," she told him. "I'm doing a double shift at the hospital. I'm going in at noon. You have to pick Christina up from school. Remember, I told you I'm covering today for Patty who's out sick."

"Oh, that's right. It slipped my mind. I have a million things to do at work. It's been hectic with the announcement of the merger. Everyone's concerned they might lose their jobs."

"Well, you got nothing to worry about." Paula kissed the side of his mouth.

"They'd be doing me a favor," Dominic said, his poor excuse for a smile fading as he walked out of the kitchen, pulling the coffee-stained pant leg away from his skin.

Paula watched him leave, thinking that the story had him spooked. She knew her husband, and he couldn't fool her so easily. His attempt to downplay the significance of such a startling revelation about his former college roommate possibly being responsible for murdering his wife and two children was not convincing. She could tell it bothered him, but she didn't know why he was pretending otherwise. Something was wrong, and she was worried about him.

*

While Dominic's position at the bank was unchanged at the moment, he was more concerned about his job than he let on to his wife. Many employees had been moved to different departments, a few were transferred to other locations or given their permanent walking papers, and Dominic thought he could be next. With few staffers remaining at his location, he found himself all alone on the floor most of the day, and without the phone ringing incessantly and no one barging into his office, it was all but impossible for him to focus on anything other than the Ethan Palmer story. It was all he could think about. He spent the entire morning searching on-line for more information about the incident in Glens Falls. He checked every news website he could find, but not a single media outlet had filed a report on the grisly murders. None of the major news agencies even reprinted the story. It was as if it had been scrubbed from the Internet.

Maybe a triple homicide wasn't big enough to garner national media coverage, Dominic concluded, but a family tragedy of this magnitude would have generated strong local interest, so he went directly to the source and found the homepage of the newspaper that covered Glens Falls, New York.

He bought a subscription to the paper and looked over all the articles written the previous two days. He found only the original piece, the same one he'd read that morning on Paula's computer, but there was no follow-up story about the killings. It didn't make sense.

Dominic glared at his computer, his face squeezed in an immutable scowl. He sat there for several moments, not knowing what to do next. In deep thought, he slowly tilted his head to one side as his eyes grew large and bright. He suddenly reached for his phone and turned back to his computer, navigating through the newspaper website until he got to the contact page. He dialed the phone number listed. After numerous rings, a woman finally answered. Dominic asked if he could speak to Jared Wieland, the writer who had written the piece on the Ethan Palmer murders. She hesitated before replying that the writer was no longer employed at the paper. When he asked if she could pass along his email or phone number, she informed him that she was not permitted to provide any personal information about employees or former employees.

Dominic knew it was a long shot, but he inquired why Jared was not with the newspaper. The woman said she didn't know, and she sounded sincere enough. Reaching another dead end, he thanked the woman and hung up. When he did, he noticed the time; it was almost three o'clock.

"Shit!" He jumped to his feet, realizing he was going to be late picking Christina up from preschool. If there was one thing his daughter required more than anything in her young life, it was routine. Not being there when school let out was going to cause her a lot of distress that could have been avoided. Dominic dropped his laptop into his briefcase and raced out of the office. There was no one else there when he left, just as when he arrived, and it occurred to him that he had spent the entire day undisturbed in his office and didn't get a thing done.

He got to the school as fast as he could, driving much too aggressively and taking risks he hadn't taken since he was a teenager, blowing through stops signs and passing cars on residential streets. His pulse was still racing, and the adrenaline surge had not fully dissipated when he arrived at the school. As he pulled up to the exit doors at the back of Red Brick KinderCare, he saw Christina looking out at him through the bottom of the glass door, her thumb in her mouth. She was the only student there, and when the teacher opened the door to let her out, Dominic got out of the car to greet her.

"You're late, Daddy," she said with a pout.

"Sorry, Buttercup." He scooped her up and held her in the crook of his arm. "There was a lot of traffic today. Come on, let's go home."

"Where's Mommy?" Christina asked, once she was safely harnessed in her car seat and they were on the way home.

"She had to go into work a little early today, Buttercup. But she'll be home tonight at the usual time."

Christina didn't say anything else. She just sat in her car seat sucking her thumb.

That night, Dominic couldn't stop thinking about murders in Glens Falls. It lingered on his mind, and he couldn't let it go. When his wife and daughter were asleep, he quietly took his computer downstairs into the kitchen and logged onto the Internet. He felt a little guilty as he did a deep dive into the name Jared Wieland, which called up a couple pages of hits. There weren't a lot of Jared Wielands, but he found that they were scattered across the country. He went through their profiles one at a time, checking their social media sites, looking for a Jared Wieland who lived in upstate New York. The closest he could find was one in Cleveland.

Dominic was disappointed but not surprised when nothing turned up. It was worth a shot, he thought. Then he came across a blog site that had a recent post by someone named J. Wieland. He didn't want to get his hopes up, but when he clicked on the link, he gasped upon seeing the name Ethan Palmer in the title of the blog entry: "The Strange Case of Ethan Palmer."

He felt his heart pounding in his chest as he read the post, which revealed that Ethan Palmer had hanged himself with his shirt in the jail cell shortly after confessing his crime to police. In a suicide note found alongside the body, Ethan allegedly wrote that he did not want to hurt anyone else because there was another new moon that night. The note also made reference to a curse that afflicted him, and how he regretted that it would not die with him because he had passed that curse onto someone many years ago. The note ended with him asking that unnamed person for forgiveness.

The uneasiness that Dominic felt had become a physical discomfort, a nausea settling deep in his gut. He thought he might retch. When the wave passed, he turned back to the screen. The additional information didn't sate the appetite Dominic had for the story. He wanted to find out more. There was a contact page, and with no guarantee that Jared would see his message, Dominic wrote a detailed description of who he was and left his phone number, asking Jared to please call him back as soon as possible.

There was nothing more he could do, so he closed his computer, suddenly feeling very tired. It had been a long day. The roller coaster of emotions had taken a toll on him.

As he stood to go up to bed, his phone rang. In the midnight silence of the house, it was like a steam whistle going off. He jumped, almost dropping the phone, but answered it after one ring. "Hello."

"Dominic?" The unfamiliar voice was guarded and fearful.

"Yes."

"Are you a Fed?" the mysterious voice asked.

"What?"

"FBI, CIA, or some other shadowy government agency?"

Dominic paused, wondering if the man was kidding. "Ah, no."

"I didn't think so. They wouldn't email me. They know where to find me. When they come for me, they'll just show up."

"Who is this?" Dominic asked.

"Jared Wieland."

It was like a punch in the gut. Dominic had to sit down.

"I got your message," Jared whispered. "I probably shouldn't be talking to you, but you said you knew Ethan Palmer."

"Yes, I did," Dominic began. "Thanks for calling. I wasn't expecting to hear back from you. I have so many questions. You're the only reporter who seems interested in this story."

"They don't want anyone reporting on it," Jared said. "Not after what I discovered about Ethan Palmer. I wanted to write about it. That's why they fired me. And that's why they're after me. It's just a matter of time."

"Who's after you?" Dominic asked.

"You know who," Jared declared before continuing. "I had an informer in the Glens Falls Police Department. He told me everything. But now he's gone. Disappeared. They must've gotten to him. Just like they're going to get to me eventually. We know too much. There's more to this story. A lot more. Like you, I want to know everything."

Dominic shook his head in disbelief. "I don't understand. Why would anyone want to keep you from reporting this story?"

"You wrote that you went to college with Ethan," Jared began, ignoring my question. "What did you know about Ethan's childhood?"

Dominic closed his eyes and put his other hand to his temple as if to summon the memory from his brain. "Not too much, as far as I remember," he said. "I know he didn't go home for the holidays. I don't think he had a family, or anyone he was close to. He told me once that he grew up in an orphanage after his parents died."

"What else?" Jared's voice was sharp and insistent.

"Um, I don't know. He was quiet, reserved. He didn't say much about himself or his personal life."

"You know more," Jared asserted.

"No," Dominic denied. "I swear."

"You wouldn't be digging this hard into the incident if you didn't know at least what I've become aware of."

Dominic shook his head. He opened his mouth to speak, but like his failed memory, no words came to him.

"Ethan revealed to police that when he was a small child, about two years old, his parents were slaughtered in a similar fashion as his own family had been two nights ago." Jared paused. "Did he ever mention that to you?"

Dominic's entire body stiffened, and his eyes seemed to turn inward as his face contorted in an expression of abject horror.

"Another tidbit of information you may find interesting is that there was a countywide blackout the night of the murders in Glens Falls."

Dominic brushed the beads of perspiration from his forehead with the back of his hand. His breathing grew labored, and he had to open his mouth wide to take in enough oxygen to fill his lungs.

"Wait," Jared whispered. "What was that?"

Dominic heard a bang followed by a shuffling sound on the other end of the phone.

"Someone's in my apartment," Jared said, his voice rising in alarm. "I gotta go."

There was a muffled scream, then it was quiet.

"Jared," Dominic called out, his voice tremulous. "Jared. Are you okay?"

A moment later, he heard someone on the line breathing evenly.

"Hello," said a voice that did not sound like Jared.

Dominic quickly ended the call and stood up. As he stepped back from the table, he knocked his chair to the floor. He looked down at his phone on the table as if it was a live wire. His lips were drawn back from his teeth, his face darkened by shadows and fear. But it wasn't the phone that terrified him. It was what was inside of him that filled him with revulsion and self-hatred.

What Jared had told him made everything instantly clear. A reality so horrible that he had put it completely out of his mind all these years, and now that it was revealed, it was all he could do to maintain any semblance of sanity.

*

When he walked into the dorm room, his roommate was in the exact same spot, sitting at his desk with a table lamp shining on a pile of books open in front of him. There were more books on the floor around his feet and still others, which he hadn't gotten to yet, clustered on top of his bed. The only difference was that when Dominic left the room four hours earlier it was still light outside. Now, the sun had long since set and the room was cast in competing shadows because of the positioning of two battery-operated flashlights clinging to the bedposts on opposite ends of Ethan's bed. There were several packages of batteries stacked atop the bedside table.

Ethan hardly reacted when Dominic entered and turned the overhead light on.

While the school's Business Administration program was no cake walk, the engineering program that Ethan was enrolled in was intense, with only the medical students' curriculum requiring a greater demand of study time. But Ethan was second to no one when it came to how much work he put into every course he took. The result was straight A's, with no free time and no fun. All year, Dominic had been determined to get his roommate to loosen up just once before the semester was over, and he thought he had the best chance to finally achieve his goal that very night.

"Are you in luck tonight," Dominic announced as he set the case of beer and bottle of peppermint Schnapps on his own unmade bed.

Ethan finally acknowledged Dominic's presence, first looking over suspiciously at the cache of booze on the bed before casting his bloodshot eyes on Dominic. "What are you talking about?" he asked.

Dominic tapped on the face of his watch. "Exactly thirty minutes from now, two beautiful young girls are going to be here." He walked over to Ethan and closed the textbook in front of him. "So put your books away for a little while and get ready for a night both of us will never forget."

"Two girls are coming here?" Ethan questioned.

"Not just any girls," Dominic said with a broad smile. "One of them is Lori Donahue."

Ethan's eyes brightened and his expression softened at once. "Lori Donahue is coming here?"

Dominic nodded. He knew Ethan was gaga for Lori. She was a super-smart sophomore. She was in two of Ethan's advanced senior classes with him. She was a strawberry-blonde and cute, too, but her sister was a total knockout. Dominic was betting that Lori's presence would bring Ethan out of his shell and keep the two of them occupied while he made his move on Brooke, Lori's younger sister.

"How did you manage that?" Ethan wanted to know.

"Well, her little sister came up to visit her and I happened to see them in the cafeteria," Dominic told him. "They didn't have any plans tonight, so I invited them up for a few drinks before going out to find a few parties. Or maybe we could just stay here and party in the room."

Ethan tried to pass it off like he wasn't interested and that he had studying to do, but it didn't take much convincing to get him to put his books aside and jump in the shower to clean up before Lori and her sister got there.

Lori seemed to have an instant positive effect on Ethan. It was the first time Dominic had seen him smiling in weeks. He engaged in open conversation with her, though it was mostly about their classes and professors. He even drank, which was something Domonic had never witnessed Ethan do before. Dominic didn't observe the entirety of his roommate's interaction with Lori, as he had taken Brooke into his bedroom, but when he came back out an hour later, it was clear that the two of them had put a significant dent in the bottle of Schnapps. They were talking quietly and laughing. Ethan seemed to be having the time of his life. It was Dominic who was subdued and quiet.

When Brooke came out of the bedroom several minutes later, her face was pale and drawn and her eyes sunk deep in their sockets. In a shaky voice, she told Lori that she wanted to go home.

After they left, Ethan didn't ask Dominic about Brooke and Dominic refrained from probing him about how his night with Lori had gone. Ethan was already drunk, and he continued drinking until the bottle of Schnapps was empty. It was then that Ethan looked at Dominic with glossy eyes and a somber smile, and without any inducement whatsoever he brought up his long-held practice of sleeping with the light on. He said that it was something he had been doing since he was a little kid. This affirmed what Dominic thought it had been all along, a personal quirk that Ethan found comforting, like sleeping with a teddy bear. When he said that a monster would come out if there was complete darkness, Dominic asked if he meant a monster would come out from under the bed or out of the closet. Ethan clarified that the monster would come out of him. "I'm cursed," he concluded.

Dominic chuckled. "What do you mean, you turn into some kind of werewolf?"

Ethan laughed out loud. "Not a werewolf, a monster," he said flatly. "It comes out of my body. It can only happen if no lights are on and it's a night during the first lunar phase, when there is a new moon."

Dominic hesitated. "You're joking, right?" he asked. "What do you mean, it comes out of you?"

Ethan pulled his shirt up over his head, removing it in one swift motion. His body was doughy and completely hairless. Dominic thought distractedly that if Ethan suddenly sprouted hair and developed a beastly, muscular physique, it would be an improvement.

Ethan raised his left arm, exposing his armpit. Like the rest of his body, it didn't have any hair. However, there was a scar that was barely visible. It ran from just above his bicep to the top of his pectoral muscle. The injury was well-healed, and whatever happened, it was clearly a long time ago.

Dominic stared at the scar for a long moment, his pulse quickening and pressure building up behind his right eye. "So, it's happened before?" he asked without looking at Ethan directly.

"Yes, but I was too young to remember," Ethan said, lowering his arm.

When Dominic finally looked Ethan in the eyes, he saw that his roommate's expression had changed. The muscles in his face were clenched in terror. His shoulders were curled forward and his head drooped, his chin nearly resting on his chest.

"Oh my God!" Ethan screeched. It was a sudden, high-pitched, fearful cry that made Dominic jump slightly. "What have I done? I shouldn't have told you."

"It's okay, Ethan." Dominic placed a hand on his roommate's shoulder to comfort him. His skin was cold and he was shaking. "I won't tell anyone."

"You don't understand," Ethan began. "There's no one living who knows about this curse. No one except you. And now that I told you, you'll suffer with the curse when I am released from it." He pushed his head down into the palm of his hands, covering his eyes and face. Then he dropped to his side on top of his bed, curling up into the fetal position. "I'm sorry, Dom," he said softly. "I'm sorry," he repeated, his voice barely above a whisper as he drifted off to sleep, too Inebriated to stay awake. Moments later he was out cold and snoring.

Dominic didn't know what to make of his roommate's drunken rambling about monsters and new moons. Ethan was obviously delusional, and Dominic just wanted to forget the whole thing.

The following day, Ethan got up late, looking a little green. He grumbled something about never drinking again, but he didn't mention anything about the conversation they'd had. They both treated the discussion as if it was something that never had happened, and that was just fine by Dominic. Ethan went back to his quiet, taciturn ways and sleeping with the lights on. Thankfully, the winter semester was drawing to a close and Dominic would soon be free of the ordeal completely and permanently.

It might have played out that way, with Dominic believing that his roommate was suffering from some kind of psychosis, if not for what happened on the last night of finals week.

Ethan was still studying for his advanced mechanical engineering exam the following morning when Dominic, more than prepared for his fourth and final exam, went to bed. He had just fallen asleep when he was jolted awake by agonized screaming. His eyes were wide open, but the bedroom was in complete darkness.

"Oh, God! Ethan yelled. "It's tearing me apart."

Dominic scrambled to his feet and found his bedroom door. On the other side of the door, he was greeted by further blackness. There wasn't a single light on in the entire dorm, and the street and neighboring buildings outside were dark as well.

"Ethan, what's wrong?" Dominic shouted.

"Get the lights on. Please get the lights on!"

"Th-there's no electricity," Dominic stammered. "The whole school seems to be out. What happened to your flashlights?"

"I ran out of fresh batteries. God! Just make it stop!"

Dominic didn't know what to do. He walked blindly into the room and heard another sound beside Ethan's tormented cries for help. It was a strange sound, like something heavy moving around close to Ethan. Dominic found himself standing in something wet and sticky, when suddenly he was struck on the side of the head by something thick and muscular. The impact knocked him off his feet. He landed on his back and his head hit the floor. He thought he might black out as the lights flickered for a moment. In that instant, he saw Ethan's face twisted in an expression of agony. Dominic also witnessed something that would have made him cry out in grave terror if he'd had enough breath in his lungs: a slimy, gray tentacle extending out from under Ethan's left arm.

The lights flickered several more times before remaining on. It was Dominic's vision that was faltering now. The alien appendage attached to Ethan was alive. It flexed violently, tearing posters from the walls and knocking books from the shelves. Before losing consciousness, Dominic saw Ethan rush out the dorm room with the monstrous limb thrashing against the door frame. He was screaming as he disappeared down the hallway, leaving a trail of blood behind him.

The knock on the head became a convenient means to suppress everything from his conscious and dismiss whatever tried to appear out of the fog of memory as self-deception. However, the tentacle found in the middle of the quad the next day was real, though it was believed to be the hacked off limb of an octopus, placed at the location by a marine science student as some sort of joke.

*

Now, all these years later, Dominic's recollection of that ghastly scene took him back to the night of Ethan's drunken confession and what happened between him and the underaged sister of a girl that Ethan eventually married. The darkness within him wasn't born the night that Ethan revealed his secret, effectively bestowing the eldritch blood curse upon him, It was something that had always resided inside him.

Still, every night of a new moon, Dominic would have to be sure to leave a light on, with a battery-powered lamp as a backup.

Paul Lonardo is a freelance writer and author with numerous titles of both fiction and nonfiction books. He's placed dark fiction and nonfiction articles in various genre magazines and ezines. Paul is a contributing writer for *Tales from the Moonlit Path*. He is an active member of the Horror Writers Association.

ALONE

by Debbie Kaiman Tillinghast

You are the specter that waits for me,
Filling the shadows where I cannot see.
Hiding in closets and under the bed,
Sitting at dinner when nothing is said.

I work in my garden all through the day,
Share tea with a friend, and yet you still stay.
A weekend in Maine, a trip to the shore,
Seeking adventure and things to explore.

No matter where, or how far I have been—
I return home to your endless din.
You squeeze my heart in an unyielding fist,
You drain my soul of its most recent bliss.

Alone

As evening descends, you slither round me,
Depleting my space and the air I breathe.
I open windows to fragrant spring air,
But when I turn 'round, you're lingering there.

My family arrives here from far away,
With their hugs, and giggles, and love today,
But when they depart, and I close the door,
Your darkness looms and consumes me once more.—

Debbie Kaiman Tillinghast is the author of *The Ferry Home,* a memoir about her childhood on Prudence Island; *A Dream Worth Keeping,* a novel about one woman's journey of rediscovery after a painful divorce, and *A Gift of Cookies, a Gift of Love,* recipes from her family's cookie tradition. Visit her at www.debbiekaimantillinghast. com

JIM'S RETURN

by Katrina Thornley

The sky was gray, and clouds slowly made their way across the horizon, lazy and useless. Maeve glanced at her boyfriend in the driver's seat. He was the picture of ease, always had been. "Calm" was his middle name. Jim's blue eyes never left the road. One hand on the wheel, the other alternating between changing the radio station and tapping the beat against his knee. When they first started dating, that free hand would usually rest on her knee. She couldn't remember when that had stopped and supposed it would bother her.

He had no idea.

Beautiful ignorance.

She sighed, believing his thoughts to be empty, devoid of anything but the direction the vehicle was moving, not where they were going.

There was a difference, after all.

Jim watched the lightning crack across the sky, reminding him of the cracks in a dropped Easter egg, or in the bedroom mirror back home...

He chased the thought away and whistled a song his mother had taught him. He had always used it to calm down, to quiet the thoughts that crept up from the depths of his soul, swamp creatures on a warpath. He was the battle ground.

The song bothered Maeve, but little did she know, she would dislike the alternative more. He had let the thoughts bubble up from time to time, trying to appease her, but would always cave when he felt himself spiraling. He would whistle the song, and everything would quiet down. The way it was supposed to. She didn't say anything about the annoyance she felt, but she didn't have to. He could hear the *shut up* she wanted to scream loud and clear.

The car vibrated with the roll of thunder that erupted from the earth. Instead of whistling, he began humming, his eyes focused outward. They just had to get there. Things would be okay then. It would be okay.

Things couldn't be worse.

Rain pelted the windshield; he turned on the wipers and watched them wave and back forth, wiping away the blurriness for a stolen moment of clarity.

He wanted to risk a glance at his passenger seat but couldn't bring himself to do so. He didn't know what he would find there or how the voices in his head would respond to it.

Maeve sighed, trying to make enough noise to get him to look at her. He was so focused, always so focused, just never on what mattered. If she were drowning, he wouldn't notice. He would be too focused on the color of the water around them.

She considered opening the door and rolling out, and wondered if he would notice. She doubted it. She tore her eyes away from the windshield and grew annoyed by the continued rain and the disturbed blurriness.

The view out the window wasn't much clearer but it was different. There were houses, scatterings of light, glimpses of faces in their homes. Her thoughts wandered back to Jim. Even though he was in the car with her, it felt like he was miles away. She couldn't reach him. She hadn't been able to for a while, but there was now a barrier she couldn't get through. She didn't know what had caused it, but it made her want to scream. But she stopped herself. It would do no good.

Jim was doing his best to keep his mind on the road. It was painful to drive like this. The silence was unnerving, even more so when it was punctuated by thunder and lightning strikes. The rain was fitting, he needed the cleansing, the world did. But he could do without the rest. Everything else reminded him too much of Maeve.

Night settled while he drove, he knew it would, twisting its way in and chasing away the sun. He had seen it before, but this night would pass. Maeve's hadn't. And maybe that's what bothered him the most now.

He took a deep breath, his chest aching as his mind began to step back.

"Forward," he said aloud, breaking the silence in his own way. "Forward."

They had to keep moving forward.

From the backseat came another sound, the soft hum and murmur of their three-year-old sleeping.

Instead of the thunder, Jim focused on that.

It wasn't too long, and his headlights illuminated the exit he needed. His hands relaxed on the wheel as he took the familiar turn. He was back in his hometown; he was returning as a different man. He knew that and suspected everyone else would as well. It wasn't like his mother to keep a secret. He had only been away for three years. He had started his new life quickly and then it all fell apart.

Along with Maeve.

Lightning broke the sky again.

Tears dripped down his cheeks, but he didn't dare touch them. Acknowledging them would only make it worse. *How embarrassing*, he thought to himself. Maeve would have a fit if she saw him like this.

Maeve turned away from her window now. She didn't want to be here; she didn't know this was where he was bringing them. Back to his mother's? The woman had hated her, who had begged him to come back home to her repeatedly. He hadn't, he had always said no. What had changed?

She was about to ask him when she noticed the wetness on his cheeks. Tears. Real tears. Since when had he been capable of such emotion?

Out of curiosity, she reached for them.

A cold breeze brushed Jim's cheek. He quickly turned up the heat and watched as road signs passed. He was thankful when Cedar Lane came into view. His mother's house was the fourth one on the left. They would stay in the apartment above the garage, the same space he had lived in before moving a state away. He could afford an apartment elsewhere but couldn't bear the thought of living alone. He wouldn't really be alone. It would have been him and Dean. But that's not enough. He could have stayed in the apartment in Oakdale but couldn't handle being surrounded by so much. So many memories. So many phantom sounds of moments past.

His lights hit the driveway and illuminated the front porch. His mother was already running towards the car. The rain had stopped and was now a light drizzle. Jim had made it; he had returned home.

His mother waited for him to climb out before pulling him quickly into a hug. She squeezed him so tight he thought his ribs might break. He supposed she was trying to put him back together.

"I am so sorry about Maeve."

"They never saw her; it was too dark," he whispered. "Hit and run. She never woke up. If I had just...I don't know."

He finally allowed his eyes to travel to the empty passenger seat, the one that had been occupied by Maeve for the past five years. It hadn't been that long, but it felt like a lifetime. And now it was over. She would never occupy that seat again. Eventually her son would. But she was gone.

Katrina Thornley resides in rural Rhode Island where she enjoys writing poetry and fiction on her family farm. She currently has two poetry collections, one short story anthology, and one mystery novel published. All of her work has been inspired by Rhode Island and its history.

WHEN THE DARKNESS ENDS THE LIGHT WILL BEGIN

by Craig H. Evans

LETTER TO MY CONSTITUENTS:

As I reflect on all that has happened since becoming your U.S. Congressman (replacing my uncle after his murder), I feel like I'm floating in a sea of doubt. I am sure many of you feel the same way, after being told by your government to adjust your lifestyles in response to the encroachment of repressive artificial general intelligence and its agents. Life in our hemisphere, being so clouded by the distress of the OneChina intrusion, has allowed AGI to swiftly pervade our daily routines. We have become lazy, and the rigor and critical thinking associated with our children's education has all but vanished.

It's worth noting that from all I am learning in Washington, I do truly see the light at the end of this collapsing tunnel of darkness. While only in my first term, fear not, my youth is an advantage. I understand many of these issues better than most of my older colleagues.

I'd like to tell you why I feel this way. I hope this story will instill in you the same confidence I have as I approach my daily duties as your Representative.

Yours in service,
Congressman Shawn O'Brien
Representing South Carolina District #1
September 1, 2036

My Story

During this recent July 4 celebration, I was talking with some guests about the challenges in Washington. At some point my mother, the elder of the group, mentioned that the conversation reminded her of an essay I had written in high school. She excused herself and returned in a few minutes with a tattered scrapbook, inside of which were memories she had collected. She found an original essay with a big, bright "A+" on it. I'd like to tell you more about this because after reading it again, I was stunned by how long these issues have been on my mind.

You see, when I was a junior at Mt. Hope High School in Bristol, Rhode Island (this was where I was living in 2025), I had a mandatory project for my Arts for Living class. I had just turned 16, so the pressure was on to produce something good. I enjoyed history and communication so I thought going to a museum or a data service center might be interesting. My mother and my youth coach were both happy with my choice.

I selected the Hasbro Toy Museum in Pawtucket. The project was kind of weird: *Pick two words that were opposites yet interdependent and then write an essay on the etymology of these words.* Knowing what I know now, having worked as a documentary film producer for a few years after graduation, this was a very deep assignment for someone my age. I remember having only one week to choose the words which I was told must come from an occupation that was inspiring to me at the time.

It's important to the story that you know a bit more about me. I was raised in a house that didn't have much: a family of three (my mother, me, and an occasional student renter), a bedroom for each, one car (an original Mini Countryman that was the pride of our neighbor who owned an auto shop), and enough money for an annual vacation to see my uncle who lived in South Carolina. Something I did have plenty of were toys, video games, art supplies, and books. My cousins were a few years older, so whenever they got tired of something, my mother was happy to pack their castoffs in the back of the Countryman and bring them home. I learned when I graduated from Clemson a few years ago that my uncle had been adding a few new things to the hand-me-downs. My mother never figured that out, as far as I could tell.

My point in sharing these childhood details is so you'd understand my choices for the project. It was my love of toys, movies, and video games that attracted me to the Hasbro Museum. It was the enjoyment I derived from painting, reading, and writing that got me thinking about an artistic-type occupation. After a few days of combing through art history textbooks and documentaries about authors and film creators, my two words finally came to me. How about dark and light? The two words were opposites, and they were interdependent. And dark and light are related to art.

After a month of research into art history, movie/video production, creative writing, journalism, social media, and artificial intelligence, it was clear to me I needed help to focus/simplify so I could begin writing. I could have taken this in so many directions. The museum director must have realized I was floundering, so one day she took me out for breakfast. We talked until it was lunchtime. After I got back to her office, I quickly went to the whiteboard and wrote down the title of my essay: "When the Darkness Ends, the Light will Begin."

I remember getting a lot of praise for this assignment. I was only 16 and my essay was published in the local newspaper. To be honest, though, I did get some help from the CHAT-GPT program my mother still had on one of her old devices. I never felt like it was cheating. Writing was so much easier with that tool. Did it stifle my learning then? I certainly didn't think so. But as we've quickly realized, machine intelligence eventually found a way to make words and thoughts a weapon against humanity. Thankfully we humans found ways to nullify the threat. But as we know, the effects of AGI have still become bigger than any of us thought.

You'll learn from my essay that I first became concerned about AI when I was very young. While my youthful optimism about the future was seriously off-target, my aims were spot on. This is the main reason why I, as a young congressman ten years later, am prepared to help take back control from the global AI conglomerates. Our work has begun and I promise you, the evil pervasive in our lives today will soon give way to the goodness we have yearned for.

When the darkness ends, the light will begin.

WHEN THE DARKNESS ENDS, THE LIGHT WILL BEGIN

(Essay by Shawn O'Brien written in 2025)

Throughout history most human artists, visual or literary, have been transfixed by the natural juxtaposition of darkness and light. How each dealt with this was unique to their art and to the time and place of their living.

VISUAL ART

For generations, painters and graphic artists have featured darkness in their compositions. Century after century, as the number of colors grew, so did the materials their work could be created with. For some reason, during the Renaissance period with the advent of oil painting, darkness seemed to prevail, first as a background and then as clothing, shadowing, or a landscape's ominous skyline. The contrast provided by a predominantly dark canvas was desirable when highlighting the lightness of nude maidens or the warmth of a sundrenched interior room. Perhaps the dimness of candlelight illumination until the invention of electricity had something to do with this.

The shift to outdoors painting ("plein air") and realism was no doubt the primary reason paintings became more colorful (i.e., less dark). This is an excellent example of when the darkness ends the light will begin. During the eras of the Impressionists, the Post-Impressionists, the Symbolists, and all the way up to the start of modern art, colors took hold as did white, the absence of color. Then, in the early 1900s, as modern art began to flourish, a balancing of dark and light colors became routine. The popularity of abstract art went so far as to limit color choices to the few primary colors, along with black and white. Cubism went equally far in simplifying a painting's design. Soon, Surrealism brought art back to art, albeit in a very avant-garde way.

From the conclusion of World War I until the end of the Great Depression, darkness made its return. Political and social commentary dominated the art world as the Realism and Muralist movements took off. Shades of gray were the colors of choice for many popular American scenic paintings. Works in monochrome with a chiaroscuro effect were all the rage among art critics. When World War II ended, it was like the lights were turned back on. Once again, the darkness turned to brightness and the colors of abstract expressionism took over. Then color field painting led the way for color dominant pop art.

During the 60s and thereafter, the variety of visual arts exploded. Colorful comic books then graphic novels were all the rage for baby-boom children. The mass production of classical art posters, festival placards, and celebrity pin-ups quickly became iconic. As the boomers got older, art supply stores and art classes grew dramatically. Suddenly everyone thought they could be an artist.

Soon thereafter, photography as a visual artform went mainstream, particularly with the invention of digital cameras and low-cost, high-quality photo printer/scanners. With the simple click of an old-school camera or then later a tap on the screen of a smart phone, the artist could immediately see their shot and begin a series of digital alterations to arrive at the finished work. Photo enhancement software made the photographer's decision about noir darkness or vivid brightness effortless. Computer and desktop printers enabled the photographer to be a one-stop shop. The print shops my mother went to all but disappeared.

Videography came along as the most recent and perhaps most powerful visual artform. Just as the equipment producing high-quality photos has been miniaturized, so has that used to produce award-winning videos and films. Digital cinematography has become the standard for decades with "in the can" Kodachrome film destined for the museums. Digital animation and three-dimensional viewing have become the most popular options of video production with color less an artistic feature. On the other hand, the occasional use of gray-scale is very effective in film noir. Virtual Reality (VR) technology has been mainstreamed over the past decade as has 3D painting thanks to digital videography and 3D printers. Holograms and avatars are finding their own fanbase as well.

LITERARY ARTS

Darkness is a concept that needs no explanation in relation to the visual arts. Neither does light. You know it when you see it. It's more complex in literary arts; words like dark and light have many different uses/meanings. Some are straightforward while others are meant to be symbolic. Over time, as writing and communication evolved, these two words and their antonymic relationship have given a reader/listener much to ponder.

Writing, regardless of its intent, genre, or medium, has always been a method for communicating. That was the case in the beginning with the cave dwellers as the merger of both art and writing contributed to pre-historic hieroglyphic storytelling. Through the ages/centuries that followed, most words were printed in black. The reason for this boiled down to historical convention: the Chinese who invented the first printing machine made their ink from soot and coal. The saying "put it down in black and white" highlights writing's equivalences to dark and light in visual arts. However, as we go from how the written words look (visual) to what they mean (literary), darkness and light become important as the impact of each word on human behavior and feeling is put to task.

Since the early days, advancements in printing machines/technology made the challenge of producing multiple quantities nonexistent. Add to this the convergence of computers, integrated circuits, and software design and the field of document management was created. Nearly instantaneous message distribution became just one click away with the user friendliness of email, text messaging, or social media platforms. Throughout all, words/language continued to be preferred until the advent of short video clips. Lifeless black-on-white print with numerous font choices had started losing the "capturing eyeballs" game to the vivid digital images and animation.

Audio (ears) eventually surpassed reading (eyes) as the leading form of communication and, most importantly, learning. First came audiobooks, the most popular being a recorded reading enhancement aggressively promoted by Amazon (the world's largest bookseller among other things) called Audible. Then podcasts became available on all major spoken word and music streaming services. Whether books, screenplays, blogs, news programming, or interviews, they all required one thing: good writers. For whatever reason, most of the writing used on these venues over the past few years seems to be dark. Novels and movie scripts have been devoted to dystopian futures with either evil characters or sinister plots. News programming is consistently based on bias and outright disinformation. The number of podcasts depicting vicious murder has multiplied. There has even been a renewed openness to a national debate about all topics related to a good death and end-of-life choices. With such a dark vision for living portrayed by our media, it's no doubt depression and suicide among children and young adults has been increasing.

A DARK VISION
Is the life we've known ending?

Since the overwhelming adoption of the internet, job opportunities for visual and literary artists surged as the number of media outlets devoted to news and entertainment grew exponentially. Competition for high-quality digital content has led to dramatic costs of securing the talent required to meet this demand. The free market's response to this was the unleashing of a generative AI technology that had been under development for years in universities, think tanks, and high-tech companies big and small. Natural language Chatbots with names like CHAT-GPT, DALL-E, and Codex/CoPilot offered an AI alternative to blunt the scarcity and excessive cost of human creative talent.

Visual artists first felt the impact of this automated creativity tech with the release of DALL-E, an AI art generator that takes a written or verbal description of something desired and then converts these instructions into illustrations, designs, or even 3D models. Painters, ceramic artists, graphic designers, architects, and woodworkers are all competing with these systems now. While many artists' customers continue to acquire their original works, preferences are changing, especially when the prices are right. Only time will tell just how dramatic the impact of DALL-E's adoption will be on the world of art and design. So far, the effect has been generational with grandparents retiring from the art world, prime-of-lifers adjusting their skills, and the youngsters with skills finding their way very nicely.

The literary arts is where the adoption of these AI tools has been most devastating. The growth of the metaverse and its proficiency with digital text and images provided an obscure backdrop for many years of machine learning that resulted in the misnomer brand, OpenAI. Its most widely used intelligence tool was/has been ChatGPT. From its launch in the Fall of 2022, a surge of early adopters, as diverse as anything the tech industry has ever seen before, began playing with it. Soon the regular cast of high-tech characters began duplicating and improving it. In less than six months, a warning from the most notable tech geniuses clearly expressed reservations with the expansion of generative AI. A suggested pause in the rollout of the many versions of this software was considered but then soon dismissed by most. The race to profit from designing what the market demanded was too great a temptation. The initial goal for AI, making the world a better place, had gone awry.

As this essay is being composed, the fascination with generative

AI has evolved into tangible fear for most and extraordinary prospects for the few who possess proper skills and personal connections. One of AI's earliest selling features was its augmentative role in executive and clinical decision support. While first meant to help users, not replace them, as soon as the 2024 elections were over, corporate reorganizations occurred and new AI in-the-workplace rules were approved. New professions such as computational linguists, prompt engineers, and AI ethicists were in high demand while coders, programmers, paralegals, and freelance writers lost their appeal. AI's convergence with robotics made machines-replacing-humans a viable strategy for most manufacturers and a growing number of human service industries.

WHEN WILL THE LIGHT RETURN?

By now everyone has an AI story to tell. Most recall dark situations where many unpleasant things happened. Inaccuracies in articles or reports produced by ChatGPT resulted in major defamation claims by important people or organizations. Exquisite AI-designed scams wiped out the savings of way too many people. Plagiarism and counterfeiting have become commonplace as AI art generation and cryptocurrency manipulation have been perfected. Personal digital assistants and home security systems are constantly being breached by AI hackers using fake voice and biometrics.

These and many other stories have elevated the threat of runaway AGI to the highest levels of government. After the recent elections, in an act of rare bipartisanship, a series of bills were passed and quickly signed into law. The regulations, once finalized, will be implemented by the appropriate federal and state law enforcement. The intention, as far as the public has been made aware, is to shut down the internet. Then a new internet will be introduced that all global users will have to register for. Proof of identification will be very high-tech, using biometrics that are incapable of duplication.

How this will all happen is beyond my imagination. But one thing

I am sure of is that the civilization destruction so many predicted has not yet happened.

It's time for the goodness of light to drench the evil of darkness.

After a lifetime devoted to family, work, and fitness, an early retirement enabled **Craig H. Evans** to complete his first novel, entitled *Why?* (Dorrance Publication). He has resided in Bristol, Rhode Island for over 20 years, and has found the perfect place to continue his thinking and writing. Stay tuned for more.

HOW MY DISABILITIES FREED ME

by Katherine Itacy

"When we are no longer able to change a situation,
we are challenged to change ourselves."

"Mom, I don't want to live anymore. Please, they need to give me something to knock me out. I can't be awake for this anymore!"

The week of March 12, 2023 was the closest I've ever been to being suicidal. I've never attempted it before, and I probably wouldn't have made any attempt to kill myself in those moments (especially since I was in a hospital and under constant supervision and care at the time), but I absolutely could not take another moment of feeling as if I was being electrocuted. I've never been tortured before, but I was damn sure this was what it must feel like.

On March 8, 2023, I underwent my third neurosurgery to date, to have part of the same tumor I was born with removed from pulling against my spinal cord. Just days before I was begging to be knocked out and telling my mom I couldn't live in this kind of pain, the doctors at Johns Hopkins Hospital in Maryland had successfully removed the tumor portion that was pulling on my spinal cord. In fact, I had been doing so well following the surgery, they discharged me less than forty-eight hours later.

At that point, my mother and I returned to our hotel room a few

---

* Viktor E. Frankl, Man's Search for Meaning 112. Boston: Beacon Press, 2006.

miles from the hospital. We had to wait for an upcoming office visit with my neurosurgeon to receive the clearance to drive back home to Rhode Island. Unfortunately, we never made it to the office visit that week. Less than three days after my discharge, I started feeling the sensations of full-blown electrocutions up and down my spine and into my legs and feet. It started when I cast my eyes down, and continued when I moved the right side of my trunk or placed any weight on my right leg. It peaked when I got stuck in bed, unable to sit or get up without experiencing further electrocutions.

We had to call 911 to have members of the Baltimore City Fire Department slide me from the bed and place me on my left side on the stretcher. Staying on my left side was the only way to prevent another electrocution. The reprieve didn't last long, however. Once I was transferred from the stretcher to an emergency room cot, the electrocutions resumed, causing me to thrash my body from side to side. Emergency Department employees had to stand guard on either side of the bed just to keep me from falling off.

For days, any time I was moved or transferred to another surface for diagnostic testing, my body convulsed, and I felt bolts of electricity course violently throughout my body. It was, hands down, the very worst pain of my thirty-nine years. And for someone who's endured at least sixty-five surgeries and procedures over the last thirty-five years, sixty-one of them occurring within the last thirteen years, that's saying quite a lot.

At the very worst of the pain, I honestly did not want to continue living. The doctors couldn't find anything on my MRI or X-rays to explain the electrocutions. They believed it was a combination of neurological and muscular complications from the surgery, but they'd never seen those symptoms before, never mind from someone whose post-surgery images looked perfect. During that conversation with them, I was thinking: *If they've never seen this before and can't figure out what's causing it, how will they ever be able to stop it from continuing?* I'd never felt so desperate to lose consciousness as I did in those moments.

Thankfully, after continued sobbing and pleading on my part, they took pity on me and gave me some Valium to let my body relax and put me to sleep for a brief time.

When I woke up, the pain was slightly more tolerable, and for the next thirty-six hours, I held my ground and demanded that I be allowed to keep my trunk immobile so that my body could have a chance to relax and heal. Given that I started bawling anytime a nurse or doctor brought up trying to move, I can understand why they acquiesced to my plea, even if it meant risking a blood clot or infection by remaining immobile. True to my word, after that time period ended, I agreed to try moving, and to my legitimate relief, I found that the pain had changed from the feeling of electrocutions to simply sharp pain. Sharp pain, I could tolerate. Sharp pain, I could live with. Sharp pain, I'd been experiencing daily since early December of 2015.

*

I've been chronically ill pretty much since birth and have been diagnosed with dozens of medical conditions since then, but I didn't identify as disabled until I was in my early thirties. Since then, I've endured chronic, debilitating pain for more than 2,677 continuous days and been at risk multiple times of becoming paralyzed. I've also been told I'll likely need a colostomy bag and to self-catheterize in the future, which has thrown my sense of self-esteem for a loop.

But even before becoming disabled, my health had been suffering for well over a decade. Over a four-year period in my twenties, I'd been at risk of going blind countless times. I'd undergone more than three dozen eye and hand surgeries over that same time period. I'd been medically advised against becoming pregnant, or else risk dying when I gave birth and/or giving birth to a child with significant physical and/or mental impairments. And by the time I finally had to admit to being disabled, my health had forced me to give up on what I believed to be my calling in life: my work as a criminal defense attorney.

Yet none of that diminished my desire to live. What did was the complication from my neurosurgery this past March. You'd think self-identifying as a "professional patient" would make me impervious to the dark side of my health, but it hasn't.

*

Your tumor has regrown and is once again pulling on your spine. But the good news is, you're a good candidate for another neurosurgery. You healed well last time and haven't developed a lot of scar tissue since then. Let me know if you'd like to come in to discuss having the surgery.

This was the email I received on the morning of my thirty-ninth birthday this past December. It was from my neurosurgeon, who confirmed that the benign tumor I was born with was pulling on my spine for the third time in my life. The last time doctors confirmed it was pulling on my cord and went in to try and remove it was five years ago, and I had to retire from practicing law because of the damage it had caused. I've had to grieve the loss of my former self, my "productive, accomplished" self, and accept that I am, and will remain, permanently disabled. My life is now filled with constant, intractable, knee-buckling pain because of that tumor, and that's just one of my *many* medical conditions. The acceptance of my new reality hasn't come all at once. Instead, it comes in spurts, with moments that make it even more difficult to accept that I'll never again be that ambitious workaholic who was able to work over one hundred hours a week for years at a time with little-to-no periods of respite. I'm no longer the woman so many people could count on to be available to help at any time of the day or night.

The truth is, I've been accumulating diseases and disorders my entire life. Illness has always been present in my life and in my thoughts, even if a connection with the label "disabled" hasn't. I was born with spina bifida occulta and a large benign tumor across my entire lower back. By four years old, I'd undergone my first tethered spinal cord neurosurgery to remove the portion of the tumor that had migrated to my spinal cord and wrapped around it. I was also learning how to live life as a sweet-toothed preschooler with brittle type 1 diabetes, which I was diagnosed with just one month after my neurosurgery. Before I learned how to do fractions, I'd already learned how to test my blood sugar and give myself insulin shots. I firmly believe that this time period marked the beginning of my type A personality, because I learned I couldn't leave anything to chance or ever stop being vigilant. It was drilled into my head that if I stopped taking care of my health for even a day, I could die. After a while, that becomes emotionally exhausting.

With the help of my parents and a variety of doctors and nurses, I adapted to my circumstances and adjusted to my new normal, which for years involved keeping track of my blood sugar levels and the types and amount of food I ate as well as the amount of insulin I took throughout each day. It involved going to the ER any time I got sick and couldn't keep the vomiting under control. It involved getting regular bloodwork taken and yearly check-ups to make sure the remnant of that spinal tumor hadn't regrown. My normal was unlike anyone else's I knew, but it felt normal to me. I even began to flourish under my abnormal circumstances.

As I developed a sense of identity, I rejected one that included "medical patient," "diabetic," or "chronically ill individual." I refused to let my health dictate who I was, and instead, tried to identify myself in terms of the accomplishments I achieved despite my health problems. Starting in my teens, I relentlessly pursued excellence to prove to myself and everyone around me that my medical conditions did not define or restrain me.

For a long time, I did just that. Having a life-threatening chronic illness didn't stop me from becoming an eight-time high school national champion in track and field. It didn't stop me from setting records at the state and national level, from competing at the Junior World Championships in Santiago, Chile, or from training at the United

States Olympic Training Center in Chula Vista, California. Nor did it stop me from finishing fourth in my law school class or opening my own law practice at the age of twenty-five.

Then my normal changed. My late twenties were spent undergoing about three dozen surgeries and procedures relating to complications from my diabetes, battling an unknown autoimmune disorder, enduring debilitating, nausea-inducing migraines, and watching my health quickly deteriorate. I was going to doctors' offices and surgical centers almost as much as I was appearing in court. My health and general well-being were fading fast, and it was time to adopt a new normal or die in my current one.

I made the heartbreaking decision to shut down my law practice and moved across the country to start a new way of life working for the federal government in a border town. It wasn't long before my health stabilized a great deal and my personal life improved greatly. Instead of working over one hundred hours a week and barely sleeping, never mind exercising, I was working forty to fifty hours a week, getting a full night's sleep every night, and exercising five to seven times a week. It was as if my body could palpably feel a great weight lifted from the decreased toll I was taking on it.

But when that pesky, whack-a-mole tumor remnant popped its weaselly head up again at the end of 2015 and once again started to pull on my spinal cord, I quickly had to face facts: no amount of mental fortitude was going to outmaneuver a recurring tethered spinal cord. I could no longer pretend that my willpower was stronger than my illnesses. Suddenly, my new normal dramatically changed once again. I went back to practically living in doctors' offices and surgical centers. I learned I could no longer sit, stand, or walk for any reasonable period without my knees buckling or my mind becoming completely consumed with thoughts of the pain.

For more than two years, I worked my way through a plethora of mis-diagnoses, suggestions that my symptoms were psychosomatic due to an inability to handle stress, and painful, costly, yet completely ineffective medical procedures to ease my pain. After puking my way through the opioid family of pain meds to no relief and being told (inaccurately) that I could develop dementia at any time, I was forced to call it quits on the law. A profession I viewed as my calling was now a point of past pride. At the ripe old age of thirty-three, I'd become a has-been.

Every day, I'd reminisce about my past accomplishments and marvel at how much energy I used to have. When asked by a new acquaintance what I did for a living, I'd mention being medically retired and then immediately delve into what I used to do, as if I were the middle-aged loser bragging about his old high school football victories, with a look in his eyes that says: "I used to be something. But not anymore..." They'd inevitably give some sort of pitying look, which then prompted me to tell new people I'd meet that I was retired, without specifying it was for medical reasons. Frustratingly, that led to almost all of them being either impressed or confused by my early retirement, which I'd then have to clarify by explaining the medical part anyway. That inevitably resulted in the same pity or awkwardness I used to experience, only this time, it was more exaggerated by the person having just assumed I was some rich savant who'd managed to make enough money that she could retire in her early thirties. There's no easy way around mentioning the medical aspect of my retirement, so I've gone back to bringing it up from the very beginning. But anticipating the inevitable pity or awkward moments with these strangers now makes me dread being asked that seemingly simple and innocuous question.

*

I was diagnosed with situational depression from having to end my legal career and having to accept that I was now and forever more disabled. It took years of counseling sessions with a pain psychologist (a profession I previously had no clue even existed) to accept that this previous version of myself was gone, essentially dead to me, and I needed to grieve that loss and accept and respect my new self. While several pain psychologists over the years have helped me employ a variety of different strategies (e.g., journaling, mindful meditation, and cognitive behavioral therapy) to deal with my new reality and grieve my former self, I still have trouble accepting things from time to time.

Surprisingly, the hardest thing I've had to accept about my new normal hasn't been the daily debilitating pain or constant exhaustion. It hasn't been the number of near strangers who've poked and prodded nearly every area of my body in efforts to diagnose conditions or alleviate symptoms, nor has it been my near hermit-like existence for the past six years. It's been trying to figure out and make peace with how my increasing needs and limitations have changed my identity and sense of self-worth, both as an individual and as it pertains to my relationships with others. I used to see myself as a strong spirit trapped inside a diseased body, but I've recently learned to see my body as strong and resilient against a variety of different diseases and disorders and foreign bodies that are intent on weakening or destroying it. I've learned to work *with* my body instead of constantly seeing "myself" and "my body" as distinct entities and mortal enemies.

I've had to learn to swallow my pride and ask others for help, let others offer help, and accept it without apologizing *ad nauseum* for putting them out or telling them, "You really don't have to." I've had to set clear limits as to what activities I can participate in, how long I can stay at a social gathering, and learn to not feel guilty when I'm too tired or in too much pain to go to an event, contribute to household responsibilities, or even return a friend's phone call right away. I've had to be okay with asking for wheelchair assistance while at the airport or visiting a museum and not feel guilty for "making" the employee push me around.

I continue to put in the hard work of self-reflection, meditation, cognitive behavioral therapy, and more, in order to maintain a better state of mental health. But it's not easy. I go through periods of time in which I work through the steps and recognize and respect my new limitations, and then relapse back into periods of self-hate or pity or pathetic attempts to reclaim vestiges of my more productive, reliable, accomplished self.

At a recent Social Security hearing to continue my SSDI benefits, I asked both my parents to testify about how I've changed and how much they see me struggle in my daily life. My father, my role model and hero, spoke about how he didn't recognize me anymore, that I was a shell of my former self. And even though I know he said that because it was his truth and because he knew it would help me in the hearing, a big piece of me died that day. The person I most want to make proud in the world, the man who attended hundreds of my track meets across the country and into the southern hemisphere, the federal agent who proudly defended my choice to be a criminal defense attorney, now saw me as a husk of a woman. And in many ways, I am.

Most days, I have but a few precious hours of energy before I take back to bed. I sleep an average of twelve or thirteen hours a day, with some days reaching a high of twenty. I can no longer sit, stand, or walk without severe pain, and need a cane or a rolling walker if I walk more than a few steps at a time. My elderly mother now prepares most of my dinners, runs a lot of my errands, and does at least half of my laundry, while my elderly father cleans the house and takes care of my dog. Most weeks, I only leave the house for medical appointments or to go to the pharmacy or local library.

Since the second neurosurgery in 2018, my immune system has weakened even further, making me more susceptible to viruses and infections (including COVID-19, which I contracted in March of 2020 and again in January of 2021). I now have significantly limited peripheral vision, can no longer drive at night, and often have trouble holding things in my hands. I've had to relearn how to pass a bowel movement (and in doing so, have had to let more near strangers look at, talk about, and digitally penetrate my anus than I think anyone would care to admit). And I have been in enough pain that I've wished I could be unconscious (or dead) during the worst of it.

My sense of self used to be based almost entirely on my level of productivity, and over the last seven years, that productivity level has nearly flatlined. I used to pride myself on the fact that, as someone who's endured a lot of physical pain in her life, undergone dozens of outrageously painful medical procedures, and been an NCAA Division I track athlete, I had an incredibly high pain tolerance. I also used to run my own law firm, working a good 100-120 hours a week. I didn't whine or slack off or take the "easy" way out.

Now, I would *never, ever* question the worth of a disabled person's life. I value and respect the humanity of every developmentally disabled person and every quadriplegic. But as soon as I stopped being "of use" to others, when I started needing help from others, I hated myself. I resented my life and my needs and felt as if I were worthless. I was unable to accept that I didn't need to be productive to have worth as a human, as if I were the exception to my belief that every human's life is valuable and worthwhile, regardless of extent of their abilities.

And when I got divorced in 2021, I questioned how I'd ever be seen as an eligible potential mate ever again. When I think about dating someone new, the thoughts that usually arise are: *Who would want to date someone whose health is poor as it is, and is likely only to worsen over time? Who's unable to do most housework or social activities and needs to take her cane or walker wherever she goes? Who would willingly risk falling in love with someone who is constantly suffering and is frequently enduring and recovering from major surgeries?* The truth is, most days I hate my tumor, and I hate that I'm deformed. And I really hate and resent that I have to disclose both the tumor and my overall poor health as if it's a blemish on my dating record. I try to deflect and act as if I'm okay with it all, but I will likely carry a lot of guilt and shame about my health and my limitations into any future relationship.

I recently realized that for most of my life, I've used humor both to deflect deeper, darker feelings, and to lessen others' discomfort at the poor state of my health. I can't count the number of times I've been told "you have such a positive attitude" and "I never would've known you were in pain just by looking at you." I wear those compliments as badges of honor and courage, and while I do think having a positive outlook makes things a bit more bearable, artificially putting on a brave face for others' comfort is physically exhausting. I do try to reveal the good, the bad, and the ugly about my experiences as a disabled and chronically ill person, but most of the time I share my struggles, they're still laced with humor in some way. I'm conscious of the fact that I still want to be liked and accepted, and I worry if I complain too much, people will get annoyed or uncomfortable and start avoiding me. It's a coping mechanism that I continue to explore as my journey continues, and as I do so, I continue to question what lies beneath.

*

My ex-husband used to joke that I must've been a despot in a former life for all the negative karma I've been receiving in this one. While I've never gone so far as to actually believe I've done something to deserve my poor health and the constant surgeries it takes to maintain it, I have felt a sense of unfairness and bitterness seep in.

I've questioned why my body seems to be punishing me. Why won't it give me a moment of peace? I've worked hard and achieved athletic, academic, and professional success. I've lived a relatively moral life, volunteered for many a non-profit organization, and refrained from intentionally hurting anyone (save for the occasional snarky remark). I've tried to better society with my non-profit and advocacy work, and it's felt as if the universe is stopping me at every turn.

But guess what? The universe doesn't care. And when I say "universe," it's insignificant to me whether it's a random set of external events that occur or whether there's a higher power planning and purposefully executing those external events. What matters is that I've learned and accepted I have no control over things that happen to me from outside forces. You know that old adage, "When man makes a plan, God laughs?" I've lived that lesson for almost my entire adult life.

In a strange way, my disabilities and the dark moments I've experienced because of them have freed me in several ways. First, they've freed me from the false belief that anything in life is permanent, or that I could somehow stop my life from changing in countless varied ways. I grew up believing in a strict sense of right versus wrong and in justice and fairness. Through my countless surgeries, misdiagnoses and mistreatment by the medical community, and the devolvement of my quality of life and ability to participate in the world, I've finally let go of the rigidness of these beliefs. What's happened to me isn't fair or just. It's not right that I had to give up my calling in life because of my health. It's not fair that my body has had to endure so much pain and illness over the years. But holding on to resentment and disappointment and anger won't change that. All it will do is worsen my mental health and prevent me from finding happiness in my current life.

So, if I have little control over what the universe has in store for me, especially when it comes to my health and the whack-a-mole tumor, what can be done about it? How do I proceed with any plans or goals for my life? For starters, I've had to learn to become realistic, to recognize my physical limitations, and to be ready to shift and pivot every time life throws another wrench into my plans. I accept the unfairness and sometimes randomness of life and move forward by learning to control what I can and find peace in what I can't. That doesn't mean I won't take the time to mourn my former, more expansive quality of life when the grief resurfaces. I'll make sure I take the time to wallow, to pity my circumstances and what might've been. But then I move forward.

From the depths of my despair, I've found my true humanity. I'm not infallible. I'm not indestructible or able to will myself into succeeding by ignoring my medical needs. I'm flawed and limited and need assistance to maintain a good quality of life. I still matter. I'm enough. I've had to accept the fact that being disabled doesn't mean I'm weak or lazy or a burden or less valuable as a human being. I don't have to exist as a workaholic or an inspiration to others in order to matter. I'm still doing my best, and that's what's important. I can have a meaningful life and make a positive difference in the world, even though the ways in which I'm able to contribute have changed.

And while I'm now significantly weaker than I was as a young adult,

I'm infinitely stronger mentally and spiritually. Somehow, understanding that I will likely live a shorter, more painful life than others has been a blessing. It's freed me from having tunnel vision and plowing through the years of my life as a workaholic, literally working herself to death. It's forced me to slow down, and in doing so, I've reassessed my values and priorities. For every moment that remains, both big and small, I want to be present and grateful. It sounds trite, but I now have a much deeper sense of gratitude than I ever had before.

For example, I know I'm still capable of doing things that thousands of others can't, like be conscious without the constant use of opioids, walk around relatively unassisted, still have use of my hands and eyes after enduring dozens of surgeries, and still have a lot of strength in a body that's endured pain and trauma. It's also given me a deeper appreciation for the greater suffering of others. I now completely understand how enduring pain, physical or mental, can devastate even the strongest and most determined of minds. I consider myself lucky to have been born without a predisposition for chronic depression or opioid addiction, and to have developed a significant mental and physical resiliency. I know many aren't as fortunate as I have been in that regard.

Holding on to that gratitude and changed perspective has been lifesaving for me. As Friedrich Nietzsche said, "He who has a *why* to live for can bear with almost any *how*." If your ultimate goal is to live and to live a full life, the negative things in your life stop mattering so much. That's freeing. It's freeing to know that the human spirit is *so* resilient, even when the human body or the universe fails us. My experience this March clarified for me that my body is strong, that it can endure some of the most horrific pain I could think of and still survive. So, whatever comes next, whatever's in my future—colostomy bag, catheter, limited or no vision—I can handle it. Regardless of the additional physical pain I'm likely to suffer, I know I'll still experience joy and intimacy and fulfillment and amazement in my life. I'll survive (until I don't).

Of course, I'd rather not be in constant, debilitating pain, but that's not something I can change at this point. What I do have control over is how I live my life while in that daily pain. Sure, it brings me down at times. It might make me more impatient and a little bit snarky on particularly bad days. But it's also made me a happier and more empathetic and peaceful person. I doubt I would've learned any of these things had I not become disabled, and for that reason, I believe my disabilities have freed me to live a fuller, happier, more grateful life than I ever could've imagined for myself.

Katherine Itacy is the author of the self-help memoir, *Relentless: From National Champion to Physically Disabled Activist*, in which she writes from the heart about the lessons she's learned from living with a diseased body—from denial to resistance to, finally, acceptance, understanding, and the desire to help others.

FEAST DAY

by Alfred R. Crudale

Only one week remains until the big celebration. Main Street is festooned with alternating American and Italian flags on each side of the avenue, and the Italian tricolor has been painted in place of the road's double yellow line. Even the church facade is adorned with a large banner reading "Welcome" in both Italian and English. The neighbors will spend the coming week preparing their yards and homes for the anticipated celebration of St. Anthony's feast and procession.

Angela Fornello has her week planned. The first part of the week she dedicates to cleaning her house, while the second half of the week is for food shopping and preparation of the big feast. Stocky but agile, her gray hair pulled back in a tight bun, Angela is an excellent cook, and her family and friends often look forward with great anticipation to her sumptuous meals. Angela's feasts always begin with her antipasto of imported Italian hams and cheeses, olives, artichoke hearts, marinated mushrooms, capers wrapped in anchovies, and stuffed hot cherry peppers. The next course features her mouthwatering homemade manicotti topped with tomato sauce, the aroma of which permeates the kitchen. It is the main course, however, that provides her guests with their best memories. Angela's peasant trifecta consists of delectable roasted rabbit, tangy boiled tripe, and cheesy fried eggplant parmigiana, accompanied by a large side of garlicky sauteed broccoli rabe. Already her grandchildren have begun dropping by to see what they can "steal" from nonna's kitchen.

Marco and Giulia Amore are busy decorating their yard for the big feast day. Marco, a mason, is tall, brawny, and exceptionally good-looking, while his wife Giulia, with her long brown hair, dark Neapolitan skin, and almond eyes, is stunningly beautiful. Marco and Giulia own a house on Main Street, which serves as the procession route, so the statue of St. Anthony passes by their house. While Marco cuts the lawn and trims all the hedges, Giulia strings many sets of colorful lights, and hangs a large American and a large Italian flag from a giant oak tree at the center of their pristine yard. Each summer the Amore house is the showcase of the neighborhood.

Festive music fills the church hall where the St. Anthony's Parish band is practicing the marches they will play during the upcoming procession. The neighborhood musicians take great pride in their essential role of leading the statue and the devotees who follow it down Main Street. Carl Dolce, first trumpet and de facto leader of the thirty-musician band, is assisted by Mike D'Amante, who is the lead clarinet player. Carl and Mike are respected by the entire parish as the organizers of the band. The two men are seldom seen apart from each other, and the neighbors ignore the overly close relationship Carl and Mike enjoy. Under Carl and Mike's direction, camaraderie and friendship characterize the St. Anthony's Parish band, which brings much joy to the people of this New England neighborhood.

One of the local police officers, Alex Giusti, grew up in this neighborhood on the second floor of his grandmother's tenement house. Each morning as he came down the stairs, his grandmother would be waiting to send him off to school with a kiss. Tall and thin, with a distinguished appearance, Alex in his squad car each year leads St. Anthony's procession down Main Street, occasionally blaring his siren and waving to bystanders. Often, Alex lets Jimmy, a neighborhood man with special needs, ride in the car with him. Beaming with pride, his grandmother often repeats, "That's my Alex at the head of the procession," even though the entire neighborhood is well aware of this fact.

As the faithful emerge from St. Anthony's Church into the brilliant sun, Father Antonio Benedetto stands on the large granite steps greeting them. Father Antonio is a short, stout man, with olive skin. His wavy gray hair sits atop a round face that houses two kind hazel eyes rimmed with round, wire-rimmed glasses. Named for the patron saint of this parish, Fr. Antonio is proud to be pastor, and his flock loves him. More than their parish priest, Fr. Antonio is a friendly, grandfatherly figure to the community. On this Sunday morning, Maria Maggio stops to report to her pastor the progress of the float for the St. Anthony's Ladies Guild. Tall and buxom, with long brown hair that flips under toward the bottom of her neck, Maria Maggio is the president of the Ladies Guild. She is also known in the neighborhood as *la chiacchierona*, or the talking machine. Fr. Antonio, however, listens with great patience, continuing to greet other parishioners, as Maria drones on about the most minute details of the float preparation.

*

Wednesday evening and the excitement is palpable. Tomorrow night the carnival will begin in the church parking lot. A Ferris wheel, kiddie rides, games of chance, and of course, fresh doughboys fried by the women of the St. Anthony's Ladies Guild will be for sale. But this evening the people of the neighborhood are putting the finishing touches on their preparations. Angela's house is spotless, and she spends the night assembling the ingredients she will use to prepare her delectable feast.

While Marco finishes his yard work, Joe Cappelli, his best friend, stops by for a visit. A lieutenant in the local fire department, six feet two inches, with large forearms and chiseled chest and abs, Joe resembles a classic statue from ancient Rome. Marco and Joe have been friends since high school. They are members of the neighborhood soccer team that plays every Sunday morning against teams from surrounding neighborhoods, as well as officers of the St. Anthony Festival committee. As officers of the committee, Marco and Joe are two of the six men who enjoy the privilege of carrying the statue of St. Anthony during the annual procession. As the two friends stand talking near the sidewalk in front of the Amore house, Gina Carnevale, known for her fondness and enthusiasm for males, saunters up, coyly greeting the two men.

"Hi, boys. What are you two up to on this hot summer night?"

"We're just finishing up some yard work, Gina," replies Marco.

"Oh, do you need some help cleaning your tools?"

As Marco and Joe smile menacingly at each other, Giulia bursts from inside the house, and is immediately at her husband's side.

"Hi, Giulia," offers Gina.

"Hello, Gina," Giulia replies coldly.

"Are you ready for Sunday's procession? The float looks great. We should sit next to each other on Sunday. That would be so fun."

"Yeah, maybe, Gina. We'll see."

"Well, I have to run. We'll see you guys on Sunday. Ciao, ciao." Swinging her hips in an exaggerated sexual manner, she strolls down Main Street.

"What did she want?" inquires Giulia.

"She just wanted to help us put the tools back in the shed," Marco informs his wife.

"Frigging *puttana*!" hisses Giulia.

"Hey! Don't talk like that on the week of the feast," Marco says, as he and Joe break into raucous laughter.

As Giulia makes her way back to the house, Marco throws his arm around the neck of his friend saying, "Come on, *cumpar*, let's have a glass of wine." He then calls out to his wife, "Hey, *bellissima*, you got any pepper biscuits to go with a couple glasses of wine?" Giulia swings open the white aluminum screen door at the top of the cement steps at the rear entrance of the house, and as the men enter, she playfully slaps each of them on the behind.

Fr. Antonio sits at the large cherry wood desk in his study, writing his homily for Sunday's patronal mass. The green glass banker's desk lamp diffuses a soft yellow glow as the priest handwrites the words with which he will instruct his congregation. He sets down thoughts of St. Anthony's goodness, obedience to God, and dedication to God's people. Fr. Antonio focuses on the saint's love for humanity, which the priest argues must be an example to all Christians, who are called to care for people everywhere. As he writes, firecrackers explode in the distance, and Fr. Antonio stops to contemplate how they sound like gunshots from far away. While fireworks are illegal, during the week of St. Anthony's feast, the local police turn a blind eye, for many of the neighborhood residents use them to celebrate their patron saint. Fr. Antonio returns to his task, and when finished, he proofreads his homily.

*

The feast day of St. Anthony breaks with brilliant sunshine. The warm morning is moderated by a gentle summer breeze. Pipe organ music and the voices of the choir waft from inside the large red brick church with its matching bell tower. As the mass ends, the faithful trickle out, but soon the massive oak doors at the center of the church facade are thrown open and people pour onto the granite steps and piazza. Many squint as their eyes adjust to the bright sunlight. Carl and Mike cue the musicians of the parish band, and as Fr. Antonio appears in the doorway, the band plays the Italian national anthem. Soon after, Marco, Joe, and four other men, bearing the statue of St. Anthony on their shoulders, exit the church behind their pastor. The statue-bearers wear khaki slacks and blue blazers. Each is adorned, from their left shoulder to their right hip, with an Italian tricolor sash. As the statue of the St. Anthony is carried down the steps, the band plays "The Star-Spangled Banner." Alex Giusti is standing by his squad car waiting for the signal to kick off the procession. The scene is controlled chaos, as many people mill about greeting each other. Some folks look for a spot from which they will view the procession, while others converse as they wait to fall in line behind the statue of their patron saint. Behind the police car are four flags, the Italian on the left, the American on the right, and in the center are the two banners of the St. Anthony Festival Committee and the Ladies Guild. Following the flags is the Ladies Guild float, which is followed by the St. Anthony Parish band, and finally Fr. Antonio, the statue of St. Anthony, and many devout faithful who walk behind the statue.

The band begins a march called "*Anima Nobile*," and Alex jumps into his car and leads the procession up Main Street. The flags flutter in the breeze as the marching band fills the neighborhood with festive music. People on the sidewalks applaud and cross themselves as the statue passes by. Just after passing Marco and Giulia's house, the sound of firecrackers can be heard. Alex Giusti thinks to himself, *damn these salutes*. When he checks his rearview mirror, however, he notices something is amiss. The flags are gone, and there seems to be some type of trouble on the ladies' float. The officer jams his car to a stop. Scrambling from his car and surveying the scene, he notices a figure atop a three-story tenement house. A bare-chested man with unkempt hair, wearing cut-off jean shorts and old sneakers, straddles the roof of the house. He seems to be very agitated. He is shouting something but Alex is unable to hear him. Clutching an AR-15 rifle, he rains down bullets upon the procession. Screams of panic replace the music, and the pungent scent of fresh blood permeates the air.

Marco yells out to the other bearers, "Protect the saint!" All six men lower the statue from their shoulders and form a human fence around it. They quickly make their way to the sidewalk, heading for a small alley. As the men with the statue enter the alley, Marco cries out in pain, his upper thigh ripped open by a bullet. Having secured the statue, Joe pulls his best friend to safety into the alley.

Instinctively, Alex charges to the rear of his squad car, grabbing his rifle from the trunk. Steadying his weapon on the roof of his car, the policeman pumps three shots into the gunman on the roof, who falls backward, dropping the AR-15, which falls three stories, smashing on the pavement. Sirens now add their wail to the screams and cries for help as first responders rush to the scene. Having ascertained that the gunman had acted alone, Alex walks over to the sidewalk to retrieve the broken weapon. As he turns back toward the street his eyes fall upon a gruesome sight. The four flag-bearers are sprawled thirty feet behind his squad car. Two lie dead in a pool of blood, while the other two writhe in pain from their injuries. Most of the women from the guild have abandoned the float, except for Gina Carnevale, who sits in shock, unable to move. She is flanked by two other women, one on her left and Angela Fornello on her right. Angela will never again serve her sumptuous delicacies.

From the sidewalk, Mike D'Amante searches frantically for the man he loves. He vomits violently upon finding Carl in the middle of the street, lying prostrate, face down in his own blood. Rescuers work quickly to load the dead and the injured into ambulances and speed off to area hospitals, while police secure the area and begin to collect evidence. With five dead and eight injured, the damage done to the psyche of this New England ethnic neighborhood is truly incalculable.

*

Eight days after the fateful feast day, Fr. Antonio is celebrating an evening healing mass for the community. This is the first time he addresses his flock. Last Sunday he celebrated mass without giving a homily. There were very few people in church that day anyway. This evening, however, the church is full, and among the muted light streaming in through the stained-glass windows, the faithful await Fr. Antonio's words. As he takes his place at the podium, overlooking his congregation, his eyes well up with tears. Five of them are missing, and eight sit bandaged. Twice Father opens his mouth to speak but no words come out. He takes a deep breath and paraphrases the prophet Jeremiah, "Look to see if there is any suffering like our suffering. My brothers and sisters, we come together tonight with heavy hearts steeped in suffering. How will we recover from the pain that has been inflicted upon us? How do we find the strength to heal and carry on? I, as your pastor, have no magic words to take your pain away, no magic wand to make you forget the terror of that morning. What I do offer is a proposal. We must not allow our departed loved ones to have died in vain. We must make our voices heard. I have organized a meeting with our representatives and senators in our church hall. You are all invited. They must hear our voices. We must tell them of the terror we experienced on a day which we hold sacred, a day usually filled with happiness and love. I have also written to the Speaker of the House and the President of the Senate in Washington, and I urge all of you to do the same. I have a sample letter which I will distribute. You are welcome to use it to help draft your personal letter."

As the priest continues to speak, sobs are heard, and many people wipe away tears. From his wheelchair, Marco Amore looks at his wife Giulia, who is focused on the twelfth station of the cross, *Jesus Dies on the Cross*. Alex Giusti drapes his arm around his grandmother, who is unable to control her sobbing. Maria Maggio stares blankly at the plaster copy of Michelangelo's *Pietà* which sits behind three rows of votive candles on a side altar. When mass ends, the faithful once again exit through the great oak doors of the church. Matt Volta, president of the St. Anthony Festival committee, is speaking with Richard Campoforte, one of the selectmen of the city. Volta asks his friend, "Why would God allow such a thing to happen to this community that is so devoted to Him and St. Anthony?" Campoforte reprimands him, saying, "Don't blame God! This is not God's fault. What type of government does nothing as its citizens continue to be victims of gun violence? Don't blame God! Blame the politicians in Washington who refuse to address this problem." They walk up Main Street, still festooned with alternating American and Italian flags on each side of the avenue, vestiges of happier days.

Alfred R. Crudale grew up in the Knightsville section of Cranston. He is a lecturer in the Italian department at the University of Rhode Island. He and his wife Barbara live on their small farm in West Kingston. In 2021 Bordighera Press published Crudale's book *The Voices of Italy: Italian Language Newspapers and Radio Programs in Rhode Island*.

AMERICAN VOICES

by Thomas Lane

The days slide by...our lives pressed up
against windows
Looking in...looking out.
Waiting for the light to change....

Beneath the small compromised steps of daily life
I watch the foundations of a nation splinter,
orphaned parts renouncing the whole,
their voices scattering like sparks in the wind
catching fire in the neighborhoods of my heart,
leaving the singed imprint of their darkness
on every vivid nerve

Today, fractured America is speaking loudly
from hardship...from pain...from love
defending and asserting
asking and reflecting
who am I now?...and now?...and now?

a chorus of impressions respond...

You are...
A vast carbon footprint on the zigzagging road of excess
a warm summer night embedded with rap music and lullabies
the practice of justice that bends towards power
the dream of rags to riches pierced by nightmares

You are...
A child sitting on the broad shoulders of a father's faith
a conman, selling misconceptions, turning wine into dirty water
exhaustion and sorrow, seeking oblivion in the drug of denial
a beer can floating in a Hollywood swimming pool

You are...
a knee pressed against a neck, awaiting a breath that never comes
a story told in aggressive fonts, rife with conquest and courage
a rushing river...thrashing against its banks,
traveling deeper and deeper into the unknown ...

And yet...
at the core of these seasons of discontent
You are...
the longing for the union of Heart & Soul & Earth
raising the rusty cup of hope to your lips,
drinking deeply...and
passing it quietly on
to me—

Connecticut-born **Thomas Lane** is a multidimensional artist, drawn to spaces where art and spirit and social justice intersect. His creations include *Hotel Earth*, a CD of his songs; *The Artists' Manifesto*, a book based on surveys; and *The Karma Factor*, a recently published metaphysical thriller currently being adapted for a feature film.

THE DELVING DASHWOODS

by Pete Rock

1790, Early America
The Town of Campdon

"How many feet ya gotta that line, boy?" Antonina Dashwood yelled over her shoulder as she pulled the vines and embedded roots from the rock.

"Hold on, Ant." Abraham, her half-brother, continued to measure with arm-lengths, pulling the string off the spool.

"How much is left on there?" Antonina grunted, clearing the last of the stubborn growth clinging in the cracks of the exposed stone.

"Maybe another couple hundred, forty-five, fifty, fifty-five." Abe continued to count off what was left for complete accuracy.

Antonina stood in front of the opening and took a big breath, looking back at the hired men helping to clear the property that her estranged husband Benjamin had purchased years earlier when they were secretly married. The lore and mysteries surrounding the area were told and retold since the English settlers founded the town in 1691, carrying on the tales from the local Wampanoag tribes who avoided the land at all costs, like a plague.

Stories of bearded devils from the ocean were passed down among the elder natives thousands of years before the English arrived. The details were vague, and the tales of strange foreign people disappearing into the earth, never to return, were cast off as myth that faded into legend.

Is this it? Could it be? Antonina asked herself if she had found the long sought-after prizes of the lost tribe and their escape from the old world.

"Seven hundred eighty-five," Abe barked out behind her.

"What?" she shot back, concentrating on the opening she had just cleaned off.

"Seven eighty, give or take a couple." Abe started to doubt his measurement count, wondering if he had skipped some numbers.

Three days earlier, one of the lumberjacks felled a tree and, using oxen, pulled the stump out. A solid slab of stone was unearthed by the upheaval of soil and roots. The information was relayed to Antonina, who quickly formed an excavation crew and began the dig. The massive slab of stone that spanned the opening in the ground was held up with two granite columns embedded into the earth on either side.

With a thousand years of silt, soil, trees, and debris removed from the area, an alcove emerged. Delving into the earth, they exposed the entrance in its entirety. A cobblestone walkway took form by brushing the loose dirt away with corn brooms. Wooden timbers a foot thick were pried from the opening, revealing an arched entryway.

"This is amazing!" Abe said, throwing the coiled string over his shoulder.

"We've gotta get word to my...to Benjamin. We might've found it." Antonina brushed off the remaining chunks of dirt still clinging to the massive slab of stone above the arch.

"What is this?" Abraham asked, stopping next to Antonina and brushing dirt off one of the half-buried columns. "Look at this." Abe dug his fingernail into some grooves carved in the stone and stenciled the impressions until they revealed an unreadable ancient message.

"Unbelievable. We'll get one of the workers to brush and clean all of this. Come on," Antonina said, reaching into a leather satchel slung over her shoulder. She pulled out the custom candle holder she had made after discovering the stone. "Help me."

Abe clapped his hands clean of dirt and cupped them around the candle as Antonina sparked some shredded fibers to life with a flint stone.

"Damn, the breeze keeps kickin' up," she complained after the third attempt.

Huddling together, they finally lit one candle, and the second with the first, twisting and locking them into the custom holder. Abe tied the end of a string to a rock and stared at his half-sister. Beads of sweat dripped down his forehead as the July sun streamed down from the sky, baking their skin.

"Follow me." Antonina waved Abe on as she disappeared into a wall of black nothing.

A moment of mental hesitation stalled Abe's legs. He looked over his shoulder at the native workers leaning on their shovels at the beginning of the cobblestone pathway.

"You don't wanna go in there." Quinnapin, the native Wampanoag prince in charge of the men, stepped in front of the group.

"Why would I listen to your witch doctor? Savage superstitions." Abe curled his lip in disgust and mistrust.

"Your ignorance clouds your wisdom, young one," Quinnapin stated and sat down on a newly felled tree.

"Your arrogance clouds yours." Abe turned around and stepped toward the archway.

"Trust your heart, not your head; it never lies if you listen to it." Quinnapin packed a pipe.

"We'll see," Abe shot back and stepped into the black void.

A chill shivered through his body, and his heart pounded in his chest once the darkness wholly enveloped him. Goosebumps freckled along his arms as the hairs shot up the back of his neck.

"Sister," Abe yelled out into the dark. "Antonina, where are you?" he quickly followed up, spinning around.

The rectangle of light coming from outside only reached a foot past the threshold of the opening, and Abe's heart told him to run toward it when a hand grabbed his shoulder.

"Ahhhhhhh," Abe screamed, completely shaken.

"Calm down, Abe. Make sure your string trail isn't knotted up. Follow me, this is interesting." Antonina held the double candle holder out in front, barely creating a two-foot halo of light in the absolute dark of the tunnel.

"Are you sure this is safe? What if somethin's down here?" Abe's fear spit out of his mouth.

"That's why we're down here. Now shut up and lay that string, come on."

The natural rock tunnel shrank in size the farther they ventured into the cave. Abe held out his hand as the walls closed in and quickly pulled his arm back when his fingers felt the damp coldness of the rock. He wiped his hand on his shirt to try and erase the feeling.

"Are you watchin' the line?"

"Yes, sister," Abe said with no confidence. He was entirely distracted by the claustrophobia that crept through him the closer the walls came.

"Keep up."

Abe looked back into the endless nothing and held his hand up in front of his face but could not see it. He let out a whimper.

"What is it?" Antonina whispered.

Abe moved his hand closer to his face, hoping it would appear, and whimpered again when he touched his nose without seeing it. "I can't see anything; I don't feel good."

"Don't you even." Antonina stopped and turned around after the tunnel shrank down to the size of a small door, barely six feet tall and shoulder width.

Abe scratched his arms, feeling the tingles work down from his neck to the tips of his fingers like a hundred spiders crawling along his skin in the complete dark. Spinning around, he became disoriented, and caught a distant glimmer of light that seemed a hundred feet away.

"Sister," he called at the flicker of light. He walked toward the only point of reference in his whole black world.

"Abraham," she called back, hoping he didn't panic and run.

"I'm here, oh thank god, I became confused and lost the light when my mind wandered."

"Stay close. Are you releasing the string?" Antonina put a hand on his shoulder.

"Yeah, we're good. We're about halfway through the coil, which puts us around 320 or 350, give or take." Abe felt better concentrating on something other than the encroaching underground cavern.

"Good, come on. There's an opening up ahead, follow me and stay close, and don't forget to lay the string proper; we don't need it knotting." She stared at her brother in the flickering candlelight.

Antonina passed through the narrow opening and entered a chamber where the candlelight could not reach any wall or ceiling. Walking to her right twenty paces, she found a wall and placed her hand on the damp cold stone to steady herself. Holding the candles as high as she could, she stared at the black above her, as the height of the cave's ceiling was still a mystery.

"Abraham?"

"Right behind you," he answered, close enough for her to feel his breath on her neck.

"How's the string?"

"Good, we're good," he mumbled.

She continued without answering, following the jagged rock wall, reaching out and dragging her fingers along the surface, feeling the condensation build up and drip into her palm.

The light glimmered off the glossy ceiling as the height lessened the farther they explored.

Curious to find the opposite wall they were now using as a guide, Antonina walked across the cave, abandoning the reassurance of the solid surface. Crunching along the gravel, she kicked a rock out of the way every now and then or stubbed her toe on a more substantial stone. To her relief, the light illuminated another wall within twenty paces.

"Abraham?" she whispered, spinning around.

"I'm here," Abe hushed out in a shaky voice.

"How far out are we?"

"Um...about 520-30."

"Alright, backtrack to the other wall, and we'll continue." Antonina walked next to Abe as he coiled the extra string they had just laid across the cave.

The temperature dropped, chilling their skin the deeper they delved into the complex. A neutral scent of wet moss and rich dirt seeped through their nostrils, touching the back of their throats.

"Sister? Ant?"

"What is it?" she shot back.

"I don't have much line left."

"Well, tie the next one on," she said, waiting impatiently as Abe pulled out another coil from his satchel and fastened the ends.

"Alright, we're all set."

"You sure?"

"Yeah, we're good." Abe kneeled, double-checking the knot. "All set."

The cave narrowed slightly and wound downward until Antonina came to a skidding halt.

"What is it?" Abe stopped just short of running into her.

"I don't know, it's..."

"It's what?" Abe's hand was shaking.

"It's an opening." She held the candles up to the recess in the wall. "But there's wood, timbers."

"What?" Abe stepped up next to her, feeling the surface. "Ow!" He pulled his hand away.

"What happened?" Antonina swung the light around.

"Splinter." Abe bit into his skin, dug the wood out with his teeth, and spit it out. "Who did this?"

"The same people that built and closed up the entrance."

"Why?"

"That's what we're gonna find out." Antonina held the candles up, trying to sight the top of the timbers, when the flames flickered from a draft as if the cave were breathing.

"Did you feel that?" Abe said as the hair stood up on his arms.

She didn't respond but kicked the boards where they met the gravel ground. Antonina's foot became lodged in the rotted wood, which had soaked up the moisture like a sponge, slowly saturating the ancient timber over the centuries. Pulling her foot out, she kicked another hole next to the one she had just created.

Abe kicked the blockade with intense focus, anxious to occupy his mind with anything except the endless darkness. Within minutes they managed to create a breach in the barricade, just big enough to crawl through on their stomachs.

"Abraham."

"No way."

"Abraham."

"I don't want to; we don't know what's on the other side." Abe took a step backward.

"Abraham, get in there. Now!" Antonina's voice traveled down the cave and came back a second later, causing Abe to jump.

"Yes, sister." Abe dropped to his knees, wincing as the sharp gravel dug into his skin through his pants. She joined him on the ground, hovering the candles above the ragged breach.

"Go on now." She offered an open palm without any real encouragement.

Abe snaked his head through the rotted wood into even deeper darkness. Wiggling on his stomach, the damp gravel saturated his shirt, slowly transferring the wetness to his skin as jagged splinters scraped along his back, catching and ripping his shirt. The smaller granules stuck to his palms as Abe pulled himself through the opening.

His blood was racing faster than his heart could pump it as Abe stood up, feeling a draft of warm air kiss his neck. A growing light emerged from the ground as a hand appeared from the hole, holding one of the candles Antonina had removed from the holder.

"Take this and tell me what you find. Here's the string." She tossed the coil at his feet.

Abe held the candle above his head, hoping to see anything, and whimpered when a wave of movement flowed across the ceiling.

"Ahhhh." He let out a soft cry as wax dripped down his arm and solidified, stinging his skin. The movement above him increased to a constant busyness accompanied by sporadic clicking.

"What is it?" Antonina spoke through the hole, echoing in the chamber. The clicks increased, and sounded like squeaks.

"Don't say anyth—Ah!" Abe yelled out. He waved his arms around as thousands of bats dive-bombed his head and swirled around his frozen, scared-stiff body.

Abe snapped out of it when the tornado of nocturnal nightmares extinguished his candle flame, sending him into utter and complete darkness. Darkness so pure no color could exist. He took a deep breath and unleashed a guttural scream that reverberated around the chamber.

"What's going on in—" Antonina halted mid-question as some escape bats fluttered through the breach. Caught by surprise, she barely dug her heels into the gravel before she stumbled and flailed to find her balance. The double candle holder flew into the air, extinguishing the flame. It clunked onto the rock surface as bats poured into the cave.

*

"Do ya hear that?" Quinnipin cocked his head and cupped his ear.

"Yeah, I hear it. What is it?" The native workers behind him listened with curious interest.

"They found the first chamber." Quinnipin puffed on his pipe. "Here they come," he proclaimed as a cauldron of bats came squeaking from the cave entrance, flying erratically as dusk settled into the forest.

"What's down there?" one of the workers asked, unsettled by the number of bats and their historical symbolism.

"Something you don't want to find." Quinnipin tapped his pipe on a log. "Come on, let's get back to the village."

"What about Mrs. Dashwood and her brother?"

"We'll see 'em tomorrow, if we see 'em at all. That's why I got paid first." Quinnipin stuffed the pipe in his satchel, pulled his axe from a stump, and walked into the shadowed woods.

*

"Sister?" Abe mumbled into the complete pitch black of the chamber. It was quiet except for a faint fluttering of the bats overhead. A total loss of direction panicked Abe more than the darkness, and he decided to take a step.

Reaching his foot out, not knowing if it would find solid ground, he wiggled his toes, feeling for anything, and felt his heart plummet when his leg dropped six inches. Miniscule in the light, it was terrifying in the dark. Blind to the six-inch scare, Abe felt like he was about to fall into the depths of the earth itself.

Catching his breath, he committed his weight as his heel slowly squished into the thick sludge of guano. Before he could adjust his balance, he went ass over tea kettle, and flailed in the dark for something to grab onto. His foot slipped and slammed onto the jagged rocky ground. Abe gasped, and his mind went blacker than the cave as his head struck the ground.

Where is it? Where is it? It's gotta be around here. What was that? It's wet; it's on my arm. "Oh!" Antonina let out a yelp that echoed in the ancient tunnel as she swiped her arm to wipe off whatever was clinging to her skin in the darkness.

Where is it? Where is it? Antonina swept her arms across the gravelly ground in search of the candle. She closed her eyes, trying to visualize the last image she had of the cave, then slowly opened her eyelids, exposing the complete utter nothing of black. She closed and opened her eyes multiple times but ended up with the same result. Nothing.

This must be what it's like to be blind... this is terrifying, Antonina thought. She closed her eyes again and felt across the cave floor, sending the brass holder skidding across the gravel, clinking against solid stone in the dark.

Where is it? Where'd it go? Where is it? Antonina scrambled along the ground. The smaller stones dug into her skin, bruising deeper into her bones the longer she crawled in search of the only light.

Minutes turned into an hour, and straight lines of distance started to feel like circles as Antonina wandered aimlessly in the darkness of the underground complex. Finding a wall would bring momentary relief and rest until the paranoia of helplessness crept back into her brain, followed by a scream of despair that reverberated throughout the cave.

As she was about to abandon all hope of finding her only source of sanity, she felt the cold metal against her skin and wiggled her fingers outward, grabbing her holy grail. She worked her hands around the lost lifeline, but something was wrong—the candle was missing.

"No, no, no, no, no!" Antonina screamed into the blackness. She threw the brass holder as hard as she could, and heard the metal clunk against the rocky surface somewhere in the distance. "Abraham, where are you?" She screamed, shocking herself when her voice cracked from desperation. "Answer me, Abe," she said. The only sounds were her own soft breathing and an occasional bat flutter along the cave ceiling.

Where is he? I hope he's alright. "Abe," she yelled again.

Standing up, she walked forward with outstretched hands in the endless dark until she felt the cold clamminess of the rock. She decided to follow the wall and felt her way along while high stepping to avoid another face plant. After what felt like an hour, the air changed to a deeper cool. She finally stopped when her panic reached a level that threatened to split her forehead apart and let her mind fall out.

"Abraham?" she called out in desperation, hoping to hear another voice besides the one saying crazy things in her brain. There was no answer.

Sensing a larger area with the echo taking longer to boomerang, Antonina stumbled, tripped, and fell more times than she could remember, eventually bear-hugging a stalagmite and embracing a stone-cold pinecone.

I'm gonna die down here. She kept repeating it in her head and refused to let go of the rock appendage. Her genuine fear and terror grew even deeper when a wisp of air crawled up her arm from deeper in the darkness.

Where's the air coming from? It must be a way out. She cycled the hopeful thought over and over and finally released her arms from the clammy structure. She blindly felt her way through the blackness of the subterranean labyrinth.

As Antonina tripped and smashed her shins on jagged stones, blood ran into her shoes, but she pushed on with reckless abandon. Finally unable to deal with the pain from her raw limbs, she stumbled and caught her hand on a rigid object projecting from the cave wall. It caught her wrist, almost snapping it as she fell. Thinking it was just an odd pillar of stone, she felt her way up the wall and grasped a wooden pole the size of a small branch.

Antonina's fascination grew with the exploration of the pole. *What is this? Why is this,* she wondered. Feeling along the shaft, she lost her balance when it dislodged from the wall, and she stumbled backward, and slammed into the craggy rock surface again.

She recovered with a burst of adrenaline, and worked her fingers along the item. She felt a bulbous growth at the end of the stick. Triggering her need for light, she fumbled in her satchel and retrieved the flint stones. Newfound hope grew each time sparks ricocheted off the damp cloth wrapped at the end of the stick. Hundreds of attempts produced nothing more than flickers of dying hope in the ancient cave's deep, damp dark.

Everything felt soggy, even her clothes. She ripped threads until she had formed a series of marble-sized, loosely woven string balls. Piling them up, she clicked the flints until her fingers were bleeding. Antonina cried out in the endless echo chamber when a steady orange flame grew to an inch.

Her excitement reached an enormous level until she saw the flame shrink; then she piled shredded fabric from her clothes on top of it, careful not to smother the living fire gasping for oxygen. As she coaxed the flame into a small fire, Antonina inhaled the intoxicating smoke, cherishing the scent. She grabbed the torch and held it over the fire and was momentarily blinded by the abundance of light growing in the cave. But she was afraid to take her eyes off it for fear it would disappear and leave her in the black abyss once again.

With the circle of light growing, the creepy crawlers retreated into the safety of darkness. Standing up, Antonina raised the flaming torch as high as she could, unable to see the top of the cave.

She held the guiding light out in front of her and floundered through the undulating cave system, and eventually discovered a narrow section of the vast chamber, which funneled into a passageway, worming into the rock. Following the winding tunnel for hundreds of feet, she discovered another torch lodged in the rock and ignited that one for extra insurance. The cave passage shrank until she had to duck and crawl, and she found another cave chamber with ceilings too high to see.

She explored the area and found it to be surprisingly flat. There was only one passageway off the main chamber. As Antonina entered the newly discovered rock tunnel, a draft of air blew so hard it threatened to extinguish the torches, and she froze for fear of the dark, but the breeze stopped. She slowly crept along until she came upon a slotted wooden barricade. Curious, she pushed it with her foot and watched it swing open, creaking on ancient hinges.

She stepped across the threshold, and her two torches illuminated a carved rock chamber no bigger than a small room, with a solid stone sarcophagus in the middle. It was made of solid rock with no cracks or seams, and the only clue that someone or something had altered it were holes around the bottom of the ancient megalith. A blast of air, which seemed to come from nowhere inside the sealed room, blew out one of the torches, instantly collapsing the strength of light in half.

Panic filled Antonina as a growing sound filled the room. The remaining torch flickered as the other wisped smoke. The sound grew louder, becoming a steady rattle. Looking down, Antonina gasped as hundreds of rattlesnakes poured from the holes in the massive stone coffin and covered every inch of the floor. They slithered around her feet as the last torch was blown out by a gasp of air that smelled of sulfur, and the chamber went completely black. Antonina dropped the smoldering torches into the snakes as they slithered around her legs. A raspy whisper spoke behind her, sending chills to her fingertips.

"What is your greatest desire?"

Growing up in the last great town left in America, **Pete Rock** drank from the waters of Cole Brook and began writing music and words at a young age, drawing inspiration from all the experiences life affords. Now living with his wife Sarah on Aquidneck Island, he enjoys learning new instruments and shoveling during Nor'easters.

ANONYMOUS

By Rose Grey

PEOPLE LIKE YOU DON'T BELONG HERE.

Leon's hand gripped the note and he could feel the fibrous paper bend and ball in his fist. Marisol Estates was a large apartment complex, but he had lived in his unit for almost ten years so he knew most of his neighbors, by sight at least. The note had been printed from a computer and the paper told him little about the sender except that the writer liked expensive stationery. Also, that whoever it was had no respect for postal regulations. Leon had not expected to find such a missive protruding from the jamb of his mailbox door.

He turned his head slowly, aware that he resembled a turtle as he did so. One did not look menacing as one entered one's eighties. He leaned down to scratch behind Herbie's ears. The Westie looked up at him fondly, or maybe he just wanted a treat. It was hard to tell with Herbie.

Leon kept patting Herbie long enough to cover a quick glance toward the ceiling. The security camera blinked a reassuring green. This was good since Taylor, the custodian, didn't always remember to replace the batteries. Security had been a factor for Leon when he'd looked for an apartment to retire to, so he had appreciated the security cameras. One couldn't be too careful.

And Leon was careful, extremely so. Which was what made the note particularly disturbing. With a click of his tongue, he urged Herbie toward home. Leon had planned to stroll to Rudy's Diner. They always included a little treat for Herbie along with Leon's daily coffee and muffin special of the day. But that would have to wait now. Instead, after leaving Herbie in the apartment with a chew toy, Leon headed for Taylor's office in the basement.

"Hey, Mr. Leon! What can I do for you?"

This was the benefit of little courtesies, Leon had found. Whether dogs or humans, everyone liked an unexpected treat now and again. And dispensing those treats to working folk, like Taylor, was not only worth the effort, it was easier than the alternative. Although Leon had never hesitated to use other methods when necessary.

"A friend of mine received an invitation stuck in her mailbox door, but the person forgot to sign it. My friend is worried about offending this person by not responding. Then it occurred to me that maybe the security camera might have caught an image."

"Oh, sure, Mr. Leon. The battery died sometime yesterday so there's a gap in the film. Still, I'm glad to check it for you."

"Anything you could do would help," Leon pressed. "My friend is tender-hearted. She hates to hurt people's feelings. Is it possible you were near the lobby yesterday afternoon?"

"No," Taylor said, his voice radiating interest. "She must be a pretty special friend for you to go to all this trouble."

"She is my neighbor, and this is a neighborly thing to do," Leon said, keeping his tone mild with just a whiff of censure. He shot a pointed look at Taylor's keyboard. Taylor flushed and turned his gaze back to the monitor.

"Well, shoot," he said, and then beckoned to Leon. "See, the paper was already sticking out of the box when I put in the new battery last night."

Leon made a point of thanking Taylor. He left, closing the door carefully behind him. If you wanted something done right, you had to do it yourself. At the far end of the corridor, the elevator door was closing.

"Hold it," he called.

The women in the elevator saw him, but she reached out to press a button and the doors closed before he could get there. Mildred, he thought her name was. Mildred Smythe, maybe. Every time he saw her, she was wearing a sour expression. Leon took care not to do this himself. It was a point of pride for him, as well as a useful business skill to keep a pleasant expression on his face at all times.

By that evening, after skimming the list of residents and writing down all the employees he could think of with access to the lobby, Leon was no closer to solving his problem. He took out his annoyance on the steak he had removed from the freezer the previous night. Unfortunately, he slammed the tenderizer against the meat so vigorously that the head of the implement flew off its handle and nearly hit Herbie.

The next day, Leon grew increasingly agitated as he waited for the mail truck to arrive. He had considered keeping watch near the mail-room but had dismissed the idea as impractical. There was no good place to take cover in the lobby and lurking around all morning would look weird. Besides, it was likely the perpetrator had slipped the note into place at the same time they had picked up the mail. It's what he would have done.

So, he watched from his living room window in the shadow of his drapes as the mail delivery woman entered the building and then left, climbing into her truck and driving out the main gates. Then he gave Herbie another chew toy and left him in the apartment. Now that the mail had been delivered, he could easily linger near the mailboxes without seeming out of place.

But when he entered the lobby, he could already see another missive sticking out of the jamb of his mailbox door. The fury in his throat spread like acid. He grabbed the paper, surprised that his hands were shaking.

I saw what you did.

Leon left his mailbox unopened and stormed back to the elevator. The bills and circulars could wait, but this threat could not. He locked the door behind him and, ignoring Herbie's heartfelt welcome, picked up his phone receiver and dialed the number he had not called since he retired.

"Leon!" Charlie's voice had always been rough, but now it sounded like he was talking through a mouthful of gravel. "How's retirement treating you?"

"Good," Leon said, giving the word a definitive weight so Charlie would understand this was not about Leon. At least, not completely. "I wanted to ask a favor."

"You know I'll do anything for you, Leon," Charlie said. This, Leon doubted. When he had left the firm, Charlie owed him, but he suspected that Charlie no longer remembered this. Still, niceties must be observed even in the murder-for-hire business.

"It's a small favor," he said. "I need to know if anyone in my apartment complex is a problem - retired coworker, former clients, relatives of targets. You know the drill."

"Sure!" Leon could hear the relief in Charlie's voice. "Send me the list and I'll get Mary right on it."

"Not Mary," Leon said. "Just you, Charlie. It's a private matter."

"Sure, I can do that." Charlie sounded a lot less enthusiastic now, but Leon felt it was worth it. He needed to keep the circle small. He fed his list into his scanner and added it as an attachment to an email. He stowed the email in his drafts file and then sent an email to Charlie asking for advice on investments. Charlie would know what to do.

An hour later, the phone rang.

"Nothing, boss. The closest I came was a same name different person, and there's no way they're even related. There was a Sidney Black we did a job for but he's living in Florida now, and the Sidney Black in your place is a grandmother from Iowa who moved to Rhode Island to be near her grandchildren. And her last name is from her second of four marriages, so no relation."

"Okay." Leon tried not to sound grudging. "I guess that's good news. Thanks, Charlie."

It was good news, he reassured himself. If the note wasn't specifically work-related, maybe it was just some nutjob who had confused him with another tenant. Unless it was a witness who had never come forward. The firm had always done a good job discouraging witnesses, whether through bribery or through threats. But there was always a risk of a belated attack of conscience. Leon felt a slight chill at the thought.

He thought about some of the people he disliked in the community—people he wouldn't mind never seeing again. Mildred, for instance. It would be nice to have an excuse to remove that sour face from his life. The management of the complex would probably drop him a thank you note—in his mailbox. But Mildred was definitely not a part of his past life. He would have remembered her prune-like pursed lips and the disapproving expression that seemed ingrained in the lines of her face.

He looked around at the living space he had so carefully appointed. He loved his views, the way the sun beamed in his bedroom window each morning and the way he could watch it set from the picture window in his living room each evening. He had chosen every stick of furniture, from the plush couch he loved sinking into, to the big screen TV, to the sturdy frame on his sleigh bed. And the kitchen? That was the best part. He loved cooking even if he did get a little carried away sometimes. He scanned the floor for the meat tenderizer head and found it on the recliner seat, licked clean.

He shook his head at Herbie and put the remains of the broken utensil in the trash. He would buy another stronger one tomorrow. First, he had to determine who the enemy was. Then he would figure out the best way to eliminate them. He might need the stronger tenderizer for just that purpose. The thought cheered him.

He grabbed his jacket and Herbie's leash. "Come on, boy. Let's go for a walk."

Herbie's anticipatory wriggles were so vigorous, it took some effort to get the leash hooked onto his collar. He was a terrific dog, Leon mused. Better than people.

It calmed Leon to watch Herbie sniff the shrubbery and choose exactly the right one to mark. The well-kept grounds had been a big selling point from Leon's perspective. He liked the way the courtyard was fully enclosed, sheltered by the high building that surrounded it. This cut down on wind, so even winter days were not unpleasant in the courtyard.

Normally, he felt a sense of tranquility there. Many of the apartments faced the courtyard. When he walked Herbie at night, he often saw reflections of television shows in the picture windows. But now, as dusk fell, he had an uncomfortable feeling on the back of his neck. It was as though someone was watching, but he did not turn to check.

Instead, he forced himself to concentrate on Herbie. Leon knew the dog pooped on his own schedule. Still, he couldn't help mentally urging him on. As soon as Herbie had done his business, Leon rushed him back inside. He felt the clock ticking. The mail would arrive in 18 hours.

He planned to spend the rest of the evening working on the problem. Charlie might not have found a connection between the list of residents and Leon's past, but that didn't mean Leon wouldn't. But the next morning, after several additional hours of poring through the names and searching their identities online, Leon was no closer to an answer.

The desire to hurl something through his window was strong, but he overcame it. Not because there might be a passerby below, but because having to get the window repaired would just increase his aggravation. He tightened his grip on his pencil and it snapped under the pressure. It was a small relief but not nearly enough. He hadn't felt this pent up since learning that Bobbie Nickels had betrayed him in exchange for an immunity package. Not that it had mattered in the long run. Leon had made sure Bobbie saw the bottom of the river before it was time to testify.

He relaxed a bit as he replayed the pleasant memory. But then the notebook filled with scribbled lists next to his empty cereal bowl caught his eye and his tension levels skyrocketed. This situation couldn't be good for his blood pressure. His pulse drummed in his temples as he left Herbie in the apartment and headed down to the mailroom.

There was no note sticking out of his mailbox yet. Relieved, he sank onto the wooden bench across from the mailroom entrance and waited. He was no longer concerned about looking suspicious. He would spend the day watching the mailroom if necessary.

A less persistent person might have given up by noon, but Leon figured Herbie had another couple of hours before his need to pee would become desperate. He ignored his own rumbling stomach. Once he caught the culprit, there would be plenty of time to get to the diner. Rudy's didn't close until three.

His own need to urinate was going to be a problem though. Prostates were a bitch. He shifted uncomfortably on the bench. He had nearly given up when he saw her through the leaves of the tall plastic plant next to him. It was Mildred and she had a folded piece of paper in her hand, the same fibrous stationary as the other two. He could feel the hairs on the back of his neck rise. He waited until she was nearly at the bench and he rose silently.

"You and I need to have a talk," he said.

She turned to stare at him without betraying any sense of surprise, her dark eyes hooded like a snapping turtle.

"Yes," she said.

"Let's go over to Rudy's Diner," he suggested. "I'll buy you a coffee and we'll talk about—this." He gestured at the missive.

"I don't like coffee," she said.

"Tea, then," he said. "Whatever you want."

There was a wooded area along the path to Rudy's. He would make sure the waitress remembered how courteous he was to the old hag and then, on the way back, Mildred would meet an unfortunate accident. Perhaps he would even discover her and call for help.

"Where's your dog?" Mildred asked, as they stepped from the lobby into the sunlight.

"Herbie's back at the apartment," he responded. "You like dogs?" he added, just to be polite.

"Sure," she said. "What's not to like? It's the owners I have a problem with."

He shot a glance at her but she was concentrating on her footing, one hand gripping her cane like a weapon and the other clutching the note. He knew sometimes it was better not to ask, but this was his one shot. Once she was dead, she wouldn't be answering any questions. Without pausing to think, he snatched the note from her and opened it.

Last warning before I contact the management.

"Just what exactly is your problem with me? What *is* this?"

He jammed his hand into his jacket pocket and yanked out the two previous notes. As he did so, he accidently pulled out the corner of the plastic bag he had tucked there as well. He shoved it back into the pocket, but she had seen it.

"That right there's my problem," she said, her voice laced with venom. She stabbed a crooked index finger toward him. "Since when do you carry a bag in your pocket? I see you every night letting your dog do his business in the courtyard. Never once do you pick up. It's disgusting and if you don't stop it, I'm going to report you to management."

Leon blinked. He hadn't expected to enjoy this interaction, well, except for the killing part. He cupped her elbow in his hand to guide her around a rough spot on the pavement but she shook him off irritably. He suppressed a grin and hurried to catch up. Maybe he wouldn't need the plastic bag just yet. On Tuesdays, the muffin special was cranberry walnut, his favorite. He could kill her after.

Rose Grey's small town sci-fi romances and prize-winning contemporary romances may be found online and through her website https://rosegreybooks.com. Join over seven hundred smart readers who have signed up for her free newsletter and get your FREE copy of "Baci—A First Kiss Short Story" plus other exclusive bonus content!

WE SEIZE THE DAY AND STEAL THE NIGHT

by Jess M. Collette

The city never sleeps, and neither do we. This is how it's always been. This is how it'll always be. Now, the time has come for us to make our needs known. We feel disrespected by the disdain we're shown. We stand united that we've earned our place. We are equal to you, you greedy human race. We've been scavenging this land since long before you. It's in our blood. It's what we Rats do. We really don't want to make a big fuss, but be aware that we'll do what we must.

Selfishly, we thank you as the under dwellers of your city. On us with your garbage, you have, in ways, taken pity. You have eased our toils with the splendors of your spoils, but I'm letting you know we have no plan to cease. We'll continue our constant scurrying beneath. We will multiply and thrive. In the end, we will survive. On this simple truth, you can rest assured; it is plainly clear we will endure. We Rodents are in this fight. We seize the day and steal the night.

We do not discriminate; all is fair game. Your garbage, your filth, all your waste is our claim. The things you name proudly as only your own, we will trespass to rob you of house and home. We pickpocket and haul our found treasures below, where the sewer gases gather in an eerie green glow. Stagnant and rancid are the tunnels we rule. Over your sewage and rubbish, the throngs of us drool. Your half-eaten pizza and warm, stale beer we ravenously eat throughout the year. Oh, your takeout boxes, in all shapes and sizes, how we love your spoiled leftover surprises. Fried, baked, sauteed, or raw, it all depends on the luck of our draw.

We burrow through your trash, but we don't stop there. We also track the smells in your city air. We hail taxis and hitchhike under your hoods. We hijack elevators for your upstairs goods. We find the cracks you thought you once had sealed. We infiltrate your bedroom as our battlefield. While you sleep in your bed, we rule the nightmares in your head. We shred your hidden cash. We lick the grease from your mustache. We leave our feces and biting lice to make your morning twice as nice. We are in your homes. We are in your heads. We will torment you, filling you with dread.

We pick up after you, you filthy beasts, you gluttons who love to feast and feast. Sickening to us is your narcissistic chatter, as is your arrogance that what you do matters. Your city is run by robotic machines as you are blinded by your electronic screens. You turn up your noses and scream with fear if even our shadows suggest we are near. But did you know, Humans, we also feel the same? The presence of you brings upon us, Rodents, shame. We find you disgusting, but where do we begin? Your extra-large eyes, white teeth, and furless skin.

Soon, your selfish reign must come to an end. We will gladly break what you won't bend. We will be crowned the winners in this crooked game. We will blaspheme your glory and your fame. We'll nibble your wires, and we'll chew your concrete. There's no infrastructure we're not ready to eat. We'll leave you hopeless, welling with tears. There will be nowhere to run, far or near. Your numbers will dwindle as ours multiply; for you, lowly Humans, you'll find it hard to survive. As your flesh becomes fragile and your bones dry and brittle, they'll be perfect for our teeth to gnaw on and whittle.

Your awards, accolades, and your names in lights will all be forgotten under the veil of our night. Your tombstones will sink into our sewers below; you'll have no history, and there'll be nothing to show.

The location of your final demise will merely be marked by the circling flies. But rest assured, rotting Humans, your treasured city won't sleep. Upon its streets, we Vermin will creep, legion strong, legion deep.

Jess M. Collette writes fiction, including books, short stories, and poetic pieces. For additional information and to view original design compositions, please visit www. jessicamcollette.com and her Instagram account @greetingssunshine. Jess lives in Rhode Island with her husband, Joe, and their rescue dog Callie.

CELEBRATION

by Michael Slavit

Memories flooded through Jonathan like the warmth of a hot, soothing bath. It was a celebration. He was in a wide field with perhaps a thousand other people, two concentric circles of celebrants. Jonathan was in the outside circle, holding hands with Rita on his right and another happy person on his left. They circled to the right in rhythm to the music. Left leg crossing over to the right, right foot step to the right, left leg crossing behind, and repeat. The inner circle of celebrants circled to the left. Jonathan looked at Rita on his right, and she looked back at him, smiling and laughing. He looked to his left, and the man whose right hand he held appeared to be in his sixties, with silver hair and a broad smile. Jonathan had no idea who the man was, but it didn't matter. Everyone felt a sense of happiness and togetherness. Every face Jonathan could see was smiling and joyous.

It was the third annual worldwide celebration of peace on Earth. Two years ago, against all odds, the last conflict on Earth had been settled. All national borders were respected, none were guarded, and people could travel freely from country to country. There was one worldwide currency, and no competition among nations for currency supremacy. Ten years before that, Jonathan would never have predicted that the world would experience peace, prosperity, and universal brotherhood. But here it was! He bathed in the happiness it had brought.

*

The memory faded and was replaced by another. Jonathan and Rita were strolling on the midway at Lake Compounce amusement park. It was a sunny day without a cloud in the sky, and a light breeze made the 80-degree temperature comfortable. Two teenaged girls approached, smiling and giggling. Jonathan could not understand their language until one of them held up her cell phone and pushed a button. Then, in his own ear buds, in perfect English, he heard, "Do you want to go on the 'Down Time' ride with us?" He looked at Rita, who smiled and nodded. He said, "Sure, let's go!" and the four of them headed off to the ride.

It was cultural exchange day. There had once been 234 separate countries on Earth. Many had combined to make administration easier and less costly, and there were now just 120 sovereign states. On this day, people from all over the world travelled to one of 2,500 amusement and theme parks. Each nation sent between five and fifteen individuals to each park, so that people from all over the world could enjoy one another's company and enhance the spirit of a worldwide community. Cell phone translators made communication possible despite different languages. Jonathan and Rita exchanged pleasantries with the two teenaged girls as they waited their turn for the ride.

*

The memory faded and was replaced by still another. The auditorium was full, and brightly colored banners hung from the ceilings. It was awards night at the university where Jonathan taught. Jonathan heard the president's voice. "For outstanding contributions to humanity's growing sense of common purpose through research and writing in psychology and philosophy, the Andrea Harris award goes to Jackson Morales." Jonathan applauded enthusiastically, along with hundreds of other attendees.

Twenty years ago, the emphasis was all on STEM subjects: science, technology, engineering, and math, and that emphasis had led to increased exploration of the solar system, remedies for several diseases, more efficient solar power, and other benefits. At that time humankind was racing forward at super speed in science and technology. But our ability to communicate, to understand one another's points of view, to set common goals and to resolve our differences was lagging very far behind, threatening the future of human civilization.

Then, at the insistence of a few, who grew to many, there was a new emphasis on SEPP subjects: sociology, economics, psychology, and philosophy. Humankind's ability to understand one another, to discuss our civilization's purpose philosophically, and to chart a course for a more loving, accepting, and purposeful future skyrocketed. This new emphasis and awareness brought about the new era of peace, prosperity, and happiness the world now enjoyed.

*

Gray light streamed through the window, and there was an audible pitter patter of light rain on the roof. Jonathan rubbed his eyes and sat up. His awareness dawned as he awakened, and tears welled up. He heard the bedroom door open and Rita came in, holding a tray with two steaming mugs of tea. Rita saw his tears, pursed her lips, and said, "Having some of those dreams again?" Jonathan's tears came more freely, and he nodded. Rita sat down next to him on the bed and put her arm around him. They sat in silence for a few minutes. Finally, Jonathan said, "We had so much potential, so much knowledge. How could things have gone so wrong?"

Rita had a tissue, and she used it to dab at his tears. "It makes no difference, hon. We just have to deal with the hand we've been dealt. And plans have sped up. I just got a call from Ray. He and Jean will pick us up and we leave tonight."

"Tonight?" he exclaimed. "I thought we'd have more time to prepare, and that we'd leave in a week!"

"Right, but Jean and Ray talked with her brother and sister-in-law. They think that with the increase in road piracy, we'd better go now."

Jonathan and Rita had moved to Dover, Vermont, just north of Brattleboro, when they joined the exodus out of Boston. By the middle of the twenty-first century, sea level rise had begun to cause severe flooding in many coastal cities, both from storms and moon tides. It was a worldwide phenomenon. Bangladesh was two-thirds under water. Florida was thirty percent under water. New Orleans was uninhabitable. New York City and Boston were at least half vacated. The world population had already swelled to ten billion by 2050, but now was expected to decline due to a combination of food shortages and other factors. The seacoast population had to move inland. At first, in the U.S., the process was somewhat orderly, but had grown increasingly chaotic. Landowners were opportunistically raising prices, and the government had responded with price controls. With nowhere to go, many individuals and families just squatted on inland properties. The government established emergency housing - some substantial and some makeshift. But demand was too great for available resources. Tensions were high and there were episodes of violence. The situation became too difficult for local law enforcement, and martial law had been declared.

Jonathan and Rita had relocated to Dover to be near their best friends, Jean and Ray. Jean's brother and sister-in-law, Dave and Anita, had a 15-acre farm in Hardwick, Vermont, about 150 miles to the north. Jean, Ray, Jonathan, and Rita had been invited to join them there as a refuge, and they had been sending money monthly to help Dave and Anita lay in supplies.

"I'll go fix breakfast," suggested Rita. "You may as well get dressed and catch up on the news."

Jonathan switched on his laptop and accessed the TV news. On the first station he heard, "Scientists from the International Panel on Climate Change have reported that the melting of the West Antarctica ice sheet and the calving of glaciers in Iceland and Greenland have not abated, as hoped. Sea level rise is now at six meters and is expected to accelerate. Some inland cities and towns as well as coastal cities are..." Jonathan quickly changed the channel. There, he heard, "Martial law is still in effect in all states with ocean coastlines, as well as all states with borders within 125 miles of the coast. Military personnel are providing some help to local law enforcement in cities and towns but are primarily patrolling interstate highways as well as some well-travelled secondary routes. Road piracy has been on the increase and military patrols have orders to use force if necessary to capture and detain offenders."

Jonathan turned off the laptop and dressed in black slacks, a black t-shirt, and running shoes. He walked into the kitchen and sat, hoping he did not look as dejected as he felt. Rita was dressed in bright blue slacks and a pale pink top. Her dark brown hair was pulled back in a bun. Rita had taken out the willow ware bowls and spooned oatmeal with sliced almonds and dried apricots. She sat next to Jonathan and noted his dismal facial expression. Jonathan spoke first. "Why are we going to all this trouble to survive this mess? What's the point?"

Rita put her hand on Jonathan's upper arm and gave him a squeeze. "It's because that's what we do. Besides, we love each other and we want to have as much love as this life allows. Now, c'mon and eat your oatmeal. I fixed it your favorite way." She added, "Dave and Anita have a great little farm. They have two dairy cows, some goats, chickens, dogs, and cats. They have a big vegetable garden, an apple orchard, and they even have a pond with trout and perch. We'll do fine there. It'll be fun, you'll see."

Jonathan tried to brighten up and said, "And they say they have dark, starlit skies, too. I'm looking forward to that." He continued. "But I guess they're not able to produce much maple syrup anymore."

"Yeah, syrup production depends on a big differential between daytime and nighttime temperatures, and with climate change, it's not getting cold enough anymore."

Jonathan looked up. "Do you really think we'll be safer up there? I mean, we'll be pretty far away from most of the hubbub, but unfriendly people could still reach us with a four-hour drive."

"We've gone over that again and again, all of us. The dangers of being in an isolated area and those of being in a populated area seem to balance out. At least on the farm we'll be able to breathe clean air. For the past three years Dave and Anita have been planting cat briar all around their property - a fifteen-foot swath of it. You'd get cut to ribbons trying to wade through that. And they say they have a few ways of guarding the entrance. We'll just have to hope for the best. Jean and Ray have taken out two seats of the 14-seater van. They've got the space figured out. We can each bring two big duffel bags, a backpack, and a sleeping bag. So, after we eat, let's finish packing and be ready. They're picking us up at six."

*

Just after 6:00, the four travelers packed up the van and set out. They were nervous navigating the streets of the town and its outskirts. Once on Interstate Route 91, their nervousness lessened a bit when they spotted a few military vehicles patrolling the road. They had a 150-mile trip ahead of them and expected to arrive at the farm after midnight.

In the back seat, Jonathan leaned back between two duffel bags. He reached for a rolled-up sleeping bag, wedged it between the window and his head, and closed his eyes. The sound of the motor together with the gentle swaying of the vehicle was hypnotic. He drifted off.

It was a celebration. He was in a wide field with perhaps a thousand other people, two concentric circles of celebrants...

Dr. **Michael Slavit** is a psychologist in private practice. He has throughout his lifetime maintained an avid interest in the sciences. In addition to providing psychotherapy services and doing serious science writing, Dr. Slavit uses his imagination to explore how current issues or trends may be actualized in the future.

A LITTLE
OFF THE TOP

By Paul Magnan

eople are saps. It's amazing how much trust they put in strangers. Folks believe they're attenuated to a world where scammers outnumber Samaritans by at least two hundred to one. *Not me, no siree,* they say. *I see right through schemes. I won't get fooled.*

Yes, they do get fooled. All the time.

The best scammers are those who convince people they came out ahead, long after their money has been siphoned off to parts unknown. Those scammers are the upper echelon of their craft.

I was in the top tier, the Grifter Hall of Fame. Having the title Senior Financial Advisement Manager in a legitimate bank does wonders to make even the most cynical drop their guard. I spoon-feed them terms like equity securities, trade brokerage, and underwriting stock issues. I show them crisp, colorful pie charts detailing stocks, bonds, mutual funds, whatever, and they give me hundreds of thousands of dollars for IRAs, private equity funds, and hedge funds.

My clients trust me because I make them money. And why not? I know what I'm doing. I've been doing this for over twenty years. The beauty of it is that they don't know the details of how I make them money. They don't take steps to ensure my bi-monthly reports are honest because they don't know how. I skim off the top of every account I handle, a few thousand here, ten thousand there, sometimes as much as twenty-five thousand dollars, six times a year. I handle the accounts of over a hundred clients, upper middle-class people of solid means who know nothing of the intricacies of finance. If someone does question the amount their investments should be making, I feed them terms like market volatility, mutability, and valuation. They sit and nod their heads, pretending to understand concepts well beyond their analytical abilities. They accept my explanations. Again, why not? In the end, they come away with more money than they put in. Just not as much money as they should have.

That money, amounting to several million dollars, was nestled in offshore numbered accounts. You think there are no longer such things as offshore numbered accounts? That government regulations have eliminated such malfeasance, and oversight in banking and finance is beyond reproach? Yeah, sure. Exaggerated claims of banking practices made transparent make my job ridiculously easy, not to mention wealthy.

Yup, in a few more years I'll retire, draw a nice, fat pension, buy a little bungalow in Costa Rica, and spend my golden years lounging on a beach, sipping drinks, and enjoying the attentions of beautiful Costa Rican women.

At least, that was the plan.

*

A timid knock broke my reverie. Thoughts of my upcoming vacation in Malta shredded and blew away as I reset my mind to business mode. The door to my office was open, as it usually was unless I was with a client. The woman who knocked looked at me with wide brown eyes, as if she feared I would fly into a rage over my broken daydream. She was not one of my clients. Dressed in a conservative blue dress with a black shawl draped over her shoulders, she stood there, tense, as if unsure whether to flee. In her hand was a folder full of papers.

My body language went into autopilot. A welcoming smile stretched across my cheeks. "Yes, may I help you?"

Her eyes darted about the office, as if looking for a trap. "I would like to ask about rolling a 401k into an IRA. Are you the one who handles this?"

"Yes, I can help you with that. Do you have an appointment?"

Her head lowered. Several strands of loose hair fell across her face. Her skin had a light olive complexion, and when she looked up, I realized she was young, probably mid-twenties. "No, I'm afraid I don't. Do I need to make one?"

"Usually you do, but I have some free time right now. Have a seat."

Her lips parted in a slight smile that was nothing short of adorable. She sat in the proffered chair and held out the folder. Her fingernails, lacquered black, were at least two inches long and ended in sharp, talon-like points. I took the folder and placed it, unopened, on my desk.

"It's nice to meet you..."

She gave me a blank look, then blinked when she realized what I was asking. "Diana Ghilan."

"It's nice to meet you, Ms. Ghilan. I'm Tom Astoren—"

"Yes, I know. I saw your name on the door, and I see it there." She pointed to the metallic name plate on my desk.

I paused, unsure what to say. Her eyes widened and a slim hand flew to her mouth. "Oh, I'm sorry! That was terribly rude. Sometimes I speak without thinking first."

I chuckled and smiled. "No worries, Ms. Ghilan. Now," I opened the folder to an unorganized mess of papers. I found the last dated report for her 401k, which her employer had invested with a prominent New York firm. I recognized the name of the employer, a medical marketing company that had gone belly-up two months ago, stranding about two hundred employees on the bare rock of unemployment.

After getting her Social Security number and other information, I tapped away at my laptop, got the account set up, and rolled the 401k over into a new, shiny IRA investment fund. I printed charts and graphs to show her where the initial investments would be made, knowing full well she would understand little, if any, of it. She opted for a "medium" risk portfolio, as most people do. All the time I smiled and reassured her that the market, despite its ups and downs, was stable, and that chances were very good she would make decent money to go toward her retirement. Her date of birth listed her as twenty-four years old. She had more than forty years to go until the day she could tell the working world to shove it. Which meant that, by skimming a little off the top month after month, my personal retirement fund would increase, by my estimate, at least a hundred thousand, maybe two hundred thousand dollars.

I printed the forms that made the rollover official. I signed both forms first, then handed them over to Diana Ghilan, along with the pen. She reached for the pen, and my hand jerked away in sudden pain. I was shocked to see blood on my right index finger. Two or three drops fell on her copy, near my signature.

"Oh, I'm so sorry!" She looked at her fingernail, which had a red smear on it.

I took a facial tissue from the box on my desk and wrapped it around my injured digit. Why did this woman have nails so hard and sharp? Still, she was officially a client of the bank, so I gave her a cool, professional smile. "No problem, Ms. Ghilan. Let me make a new copy for you."

"Oh, don't go to the trouble, this is fine." She pushed the blood-stained document into the folder with the rest of her papers. "Thank you so much for doing this for me, Mr. Astoren. But I have one last question. Can I trust you?"

I looked at her and shuddered with a sudden chill. Who asked that sort of question in a professional setting like this? Nevertheless, I quickly smiled and assured her that she could trust me, citing various regulations I had several ways of getting around.

She nodded, pushed her chair back, and walked to the door. Before exiting, she looked at the fingernail that had punctured me and licked away the blood.

I stared at the empty doorway, my stomach twisting into a knot. I bandaged my finger and tried to settle my mind. Other clients were coming. It took a lot of effort to rebuild my mask of professionalism.

*

A few weeks went by. I managed to place the disturbing image of Diana Ghilan licking away my blood in a back room of my mind. I had a job to do. I had money to fleece.

Speaking of my strange, new client, I opened her account on my laptop. As usual, I had chosen the right mix of stocks and bonds. The account was up four thousand dollars. Nice. With a few manufactured losses here and there, I gave myself the gift of fifteen hundred bucks. That would buy a lot of bandages. Thank you, Diana Ghilan!

Pain sliced across my temple. What the...my hand flew to my head. I looked at my palm, expecting to see blood. There was none, and as quickly as the pain had come, it was gone.

It was nothing serious, that was apparent. My imagination, most likely. I pushed the thought away and went to work on other clients. The market this month had been kind to them and, in extension, to me. As I shaved off a few more thousand here and there, darkness eclipsed my office. I looked out the window. The parking lot was bathed in bright sunlight. yet shadows settled around my eyes. I struggled to breathe. Was I having a heart attack? I closed the laptop and reached for my chest. My heart rate, though increased, was strong and steady. I sucked in a breath and was relieved that my lungs expanded without effort.

I decided to take the rest of the day off. I needed a break.

*

I'd never had a migraine in my life. Over the past week, I've had four of them. They were worse than any hangover I ever had. It would start at the top of my head, as if someone had hit me with a hammer. Red, inflamed cracks then radiated out, encompassing my brain, and gathered in broken shards at the base of my skull. Any light, any sound, caused the shards to grind together. All I could do was lie down in a darkened room until the awful throbbing died away. It took me a full day to recover from the most recent attack.

My boss, the branch manager, told me I should see a doctor. I lied and promised I would. Meanwhile, I continued to make "corrections" to my clients' accounts. When they got their monthly statements, they saw they made money. No questions were asked. They were happy. My unnumbered accounts got fatter. I was happy.

The migraines increased in frequency and intensity. I got nosebleeds. When my ears leaked blood, I wondered if I shouldn't see a doctor, after all.

Then Diana Ghilan called.

*

I pride myself on being the consummate professional when I am at the bank. My suits are always pressed and clean, and my personal grooming is spot-on: freshly showered and shaved, hair combed to perfection, fingernails clean, teeth white and breath pleasant and minty.

Today was the exception to that rule. After a night of nauseating pain when it seemed my brain would shatter my skull, my clothes were rumpled, my tie loose, and my hair looked like I had spent the night in a forest. The tellers and clerks looked at me in shock but said nothing; nevertheless, I knew the branch manager would hear of this. I didn't care.

Diana Ghilan arrived precisely at 9:30. Unlike the first time we met, she walked with surety, her face set with a confident gravitas that sent ice water running through me. She wore a bright red dress, and when she sat down the hem rode up her thighs, giving me a view that, ordinarily, I would enjoy, but now filled me with inexplicable dread. Her brown eyes studied me, as if I were an insect under a microscope.

She smiled, which further unnerved me. "So, Mr. Astoren, how was your vacation in Malta?"

What? I had never mentioned that during our first meeting. "Um, I had to cancel. I had some—medical issues."

The smile never faded. "Oh, I'm sorry to hear that. I imagine you lost your deposit. All that hard-earned money, gone."

My heart pounded against my rib cage. Ghilan leaned forward, placing her hands on her knees. The tips of the black, lacquered fingernails were tinged red, as if my blood still stained them. My chest hollowed out, and I was suddenly light-headed.

"What can I do for you today, Ms. Ghilan?" I asked in a voice barely more than a whisper.

Her smile broadened, became otherworldly, with teeth sharp as blades. "I see you are unwell, Mr. Astoren."

Pain exploded in my head. I moaned and lowered my face into my arms. I tasted copper as blood ran from my nose and down my throat.

"'A little off the top,' isn't that how you refer to it?" Ghilan's voice was deep and gravelly. "You justify it by investing others' money in ways that make a profit, so, you rationalize, why not skim some of those earnings for yourself, to complement the generous salary you are already paid by the bank?"

A spike of agony tore through my brain. How did she know? Fighting the maelstrom my thoughts had become, I looked up. I wish I hadn't.

The mousy yet cute young woman was gone; in her place was something I could only describe as reptilian. Her eyes were yellow, with slit pupils. Her skin was coarse, scaly. She still wore the red dress, which now seemed a perversion on her new form.

"Your little euphemism means nothing but thievery." A long, purple tongue darted out of her mouth and licked needlelike teeth. "You, Thomas Astoren, are nothing but a pilferer. You have stolen from a multitude of people who placed their trust in you."

Those terrible, lambent eyes seared into me. "I asked you if you could be trusted. I gave you an opportunity to absolve yourself through honesty. But you lied and said 'yes.'"

The monster raised her hands. The nails were razor-tipped claws. Her arms shot forward and she grasped me on either side of my head. I tried to call for help but I had no voice. The talons sank into my skull. If

I screamed, nobody heard. My brain burst into a white-hot supernova.

The claws retracted and were pulled away. How was it I was alive? Blood trickled down my temples, and with it all clear thought.

Her lipless mouth pulled back in a grin. "Like you, I took a little off the top. How does it feel to have something that is unquestioningly yours taken away?"

I couldn't answer. My tongue was a dead weight in my mouth. My lower jaw hung open, and saliva dribbled out. I couldn't speak. I couldn't move. My thoughts misfired, a synapses trainwreck.

The creature morphed back into the woman I knew as Diana Ghilan. Her eyes shone with vindication, but when she got to the office door and opened it, her face became a mask of convincing distress.

"Somebody, please, call for help! I think Mr. Astoren had a stroke!"

There was a second of shocked disbelief, then people rushed to the door to look at me. Some whipped out their phones to, I presume, dial 9-1-1. Not that it would matter. My senses were shutting down. One of the loan officers stupidly called out my name, as if that would help. My vision darkened and sound became cotton in my ears. From somewhere, I heard the branch manager say, "I *told* him he needed to see a doctor," before the remainder of his pompous words melted into goo.

Diana Ghilan looked at me, her pupils once again slitted and her smile a vicious nightmare. Her voice boomed within the splintered remains of my skull. *The eighth circle, with its darkness and serpents, welcomes you, Astoren. See what good your stolen money does there. Enjoy eternity.*

Paul Magnan has been writing stories for years. His work has recently appeared in the ARIA anthology "Iconic Rhode Island" and in "We Are Providence," a Lovecraft-themed anthology. He has written a dark fantasy series, "Kyu, The Unknown," and a short story collection, "Veering from the Straight and Narrow." He lives with his family in the wilds of Rhode Island.

A PORTAL TO THE PALATINE LIGHT

by Kelly Swan Taylor

The ghostly darkness of night fades into twilight, illuminated by a rising and brilliantly hopeful sun.

"Race you home, Will! Last one's a rotten egg!"

And in trouble, Will groaned to himself, panting over the handlebars of his electric-blue mountain bike. As his younger sister's bike tires faded into the distance, he kicked off down the rutted asphalt, zooming past houses clad in weathered wood shingles, intermittently lit by twinkling Christmas lights. He pedaled at breakneck speed to beat the imminent sunrise. If his parents discovered he'd sneaked out, he was in for it, especially with Blaire tagging along.

Overhead, an ominous gray cloud finally burst its dams, pelting down shards of freezing rain. "Seriously?" Will grumbled, his breath puffing out a smoke signal in his bike's wake. As his eyes welled with icy water, he cursed himself for venturing out in late New England December. But he couldn't resist taking his new Christmas present for a spin, even if it was still dark.

Squinting to focus on the tail end of Blaire's hot-pink bicycle, Will hit something massive and was launched airborne. Landing with a thud, he was face-to-face with his nemesis: the dreaded pothole. *Typical!* The only thing more Rhode Island than its clams was its potholes.

His jeans now soaked through with a gaping hole freshly formed in the right knee, Will smacked the sopping ground around him, shouting, "Argh!" into the darkness. No way he was going to hide *this* from his parents. Why couldn't he grow up somewhere with palm trees, no winters, and certainly fewer potholes? But as the familiar scent of saltwater wafted around him amid the nearby crash of waves, he was earnestly thankful this island and oceanside town was his home.

Scooping himself off the icy road with a grunt, Will lost his footing, almost landing in a drowned hole of pavement the size of the entire state. As he leaned forward, beams of early morning light cut through the surrounding darkness and fell upon the pool of water, reflecting a rippling image of orange flames. He hesitantly inched forward, and his breath hitched as he made out the image of an engulfed ship amid the relentless inferno. It was a three-mast one, like in those pirate movies. Scratching his head, he felt for a bump. Did he hit it on his downward journey to the pavement? "Serves you right for leaving your helmet at home," Blaire will scold. But upon further exploration, all he could find was his drenched scalp. No bump.

With a shrug, he tapped the puddle with his index finger, stirring up ripples that dissolved the fiery ship, replacing it with a face of disheveled brown waves and deep blue eyes. He chuckled to himself. Just his own reflection. Yet, it wasn't. This boy was filthy, rail-thin, and dressed in raggedy clothing from some earlier time. And he also looked *absolutely terrified*.

Blinking away frosty raindrops, Will focused on the undulating image. And then it too blinked. Staring him squarely in the eyes, it cried out, *"Hilfe!"*

Will's heart was in his throat; he couldn't seem to find his voice. The boy repeated himself several times, his fearful gaze piercing through Will, making his dripping hair stand on end. *What language was he speaking? German?*

In one large ripple, the boy disappeared, replaced again by the flicker of the burning ship on rough, high seas, its sails whipping in snowy gusts. Scarcely able to believe his eyes, Will reached toward the ghostly iridescent glow. As it wavered like a flaming torch, the raw, pink skin of his extended palm burned. "Ouch!" He ripped his hand from the puddle only to have it snatched back in an instant.

With a shocking jolt of bone-chilling saltwater, an extended hand yanked Will through the surface of the flooded pothole. Sinking, spinning, he gasped for air in the frigid confines of darkness, until he was jerked above moving water. His head bobbed over billowing waves for a moment, before he was dragged yet again, this time up and over, onto hard, wooden planks. Now, on his hands and knees, he lifted his chin and was eye to eye with his pothole reflection. Coughing and spitting out bitter saltwater, he opened his mouth to address the boy. Only, when he thoroughly considered this person's tattered appearance, sparkling blue eyes, and long hair tucked into a messy bun, it was in fact a *girl*.

"Help!" she shouted. Will was bewildered. How could he now understand her? Shaking the thought off with a shiver, he stumbled to his feet and stared up at the gigantic masts of a ship, thrashing overhead in violent gusts amid a snowstorm. Above him, through the snow, was a blackened sky dotted with twinkling stars. The view was almost beautifully tranquil if the scene wasn't so frightening. A combination of raw fear and excitement stirred inside him.

As he attempted to steady himself on the rocking vessel, he turned to the girl crawling on all fours, searching the listing deck. "Where are we?"

"The *Augusta*. We're sinking!" Her tearstained cheeks glistened as her eyelashes batted away fresh-falling snowflakes. A dark shadow of despair hung over her that solicited another shudder from Will.

Without warning, the ship tilted dramatically, throwing Will onto the deck floor alongside the frantic girl. "What are you looking for?" he managed, rubbing his sore torso as a wave of nausea whirled through his gut. If this was some sort of bizarre dream, it certainly felt real. Painfully real.

Before she could answer, a burly man with a dark, untamed beard approached from below deck. Guided by the wavering light of his oil lamp, he breathlessly lugged a heavy iron chest behind him. "Abandon ship! She's run aground and is coming apart!" his gruff voice yelled into the night.

Will grabbed the girl's arm. "We need to go. Now!"

Swatting him away, her arm flew back wildly, knocking over a lone wooden barrel behind her. As its contents spilled onto the floorboards, the thick, stinging scent of alcohol filled the snow-laden air. "I'm not leaving! Not without my sister!" Tears trailed down her rosy cheeks, melting fresh snowflakes.

Suddenly, blustery gusts pitched the ship onto its side, tossing Will, the girl, and the burly man along with it. The torch was thrown into the black sky, suspended in a fiery arch before crashing onto the now soaked main deck floor with an explosive ignition. *Oh no!*

"Good luck, mates! Every man for himself!" the burly man barked. Shrugging, he discarded his treasure chest with a push. He heaved himself overboard and disappeared into the blinding snowstorm. As a scream cut through the frigid gusts, Will wasn't sure if he was hearing his own voice but was now certain this ship was doomed.

"Maria!" The girl rushed toward a corner of the deck where a tiny child lay ashen while taking in shallow breaths. Seeing her wide chestnut eyes, eerily like his sister Blaire's, Will gasped. With a weak cry, the child reached toward her leg, trapped under the abandoned treasure chest. As her older sister attempted to free her, another battering wave rocked the ship. "Help! Please!" she begged, choking back tears.

Still regaining his footing while stumbling over the slippery floorboards, Will hurried toward the iron chest. "Quick! Lift the other side."

As the two raised the chest, the ship jostled little Maria out from underneath. With a strength he never knew he possessed, Will scooped up her threadlike figure and carried her. He reached the bow of the ship just as the girl screamed, "Fire!" Will's eyes bulged at the fuel-soaked deck fully consumed by flames.

"Hurry!" he shouted. They carried Maria off the grounded ship, wading across violent, ink-black waves along the sandbar and rocky coastline. Several times, they were knocked to and fro, their waterlogged clothing dragged back toward the ill-fated vessel. When they finally collapsed onto the shore, and placed the child gently on the sand, a man and woman raced to Maria, relief on their faces.

The girl turned to Will and embraced him tightly. "We were doomed. I am forever grateful, sir." As she watched her family, reuniting on the beach, the darkened shadow lifted, leaving a brilliant light in her eyes.

"The name's Will. What's yours?"

"I'm Catharina." As snow whipped around them in horizontal blasts, she pressed a warm kiss on his cheek. "Thank you, my dear Will." He raised his hand to his heated cheek and stood there speechless as Catharina returned to her family's side.

The thick stench of smoke jarred Will from the touching reunion, obscuring the view. He turned to the adjacent ship, now completely ablaze with dazzling light. Out of nowhere, one ferocious crash of water consumed Will, towing him back into the tumultuous seas. He fought back choking waves, attempting to stay afloat, but the imposing ocean was intent to swallow him whole. Spinning, sinking, deeper and deeper under the dark abyss. Just when he thought he'd never again see light, he heard, "Will! You okay?"

Jolting upright, his head still spinning, he blinked away wet snowflakes to reveal Blaire's familiar chestnut gaze. "Where are we?"

"Block Island, silly. You wrecked your bike and your head too, I guess!" she teased, tapping her finger to his temple.

Will's eyes flicked from his overturned bike to the pothole. He leaned into the puddle, brushing away fresh snow. But there was nothing. No ship. No Catharina. Just his bemused reflection illuminated by the sunrise. "But. The burning ship. I saw it."

Blaire's eyes widened. "What burning ship? Like the ghost ship? The Palatine Light? You really did hit your head!" Her adorable giggle warmed the wintry air as she helped him off the pavement.

"I guess I did," he said, massaging his forehead before retrieving his bike and mounting it. "It's not wrecked, just dinged." But as he started to pedal off, his heart stopped. Was that a scorch mark on the bottom of his jeans? "No way!" Peering back and down at the pothole, he swore he saw the silhouette of a blazing ship . . . before it disappeared in a ripple.

Grinning, Will kicked off down the quiet streets, splashing puddles along the way. He caught up with Blaire just as the wintery sunrise cast streaks of fiery orange and red over the ocean's horizon, like an ill-fated ship from long ago.

Kelly Swan Taylor is the author of *The Winning Ingredient* (YA) and the sleuthy series *The Wright Detective* (MG). Growing up immersed in beloved "teen" novels, she now crafts stories that bridge the gap between middle grade and young adult fiction. She is the founder of Link Press, an imprint dedicated to bringing these stories to young readers.

DUAL DIARIES

by *Theresa Schimmel*

MAY 1, 1959

Pirelli pulled me from the yard today. I'm back on the ship. I freeze my ass off out in the yard all goddamn winter, and now that the weather is nice, I get put on the ship. Jacobs and Sosnowski also got pulled. Launch date is looming on this baby, and the inspector wants some joints redone. Today we were in the missile compartment. She's designed for sixteen Polaris missiles and six 21-inch torpedo tubes. Need to check in with equipment tomorrow for a new pair of welding goggles. Found a crack in mine today. Arms ache like hell from lifting that torch all day. Jacobs spelled me some in the afternoon, and I filled in my paperwork for Pirelli.

MAY 4, 1959

Work stopped briefly at the shipyard today. Piece of scaffolding gave way and two guys fell. Word has it that one of them might not make it. I was on my lunch break when it happened, so heard all the commotion. I saw the damaged area. Christ. I was working on that same beam two months ago.

MAY 7, 1959

Everyone's on edge around here since the accident. Hadn't seen a safety inspector in months and now they're thicker than flies on a dead cat. Got new goggles and a new mask to boot. Today's job was in the forward compartment. It was a long stretch that needed grinding; really a two-person job, but Sosnowski's such a big lard, he couldn't fit through the pipe. Spent most of the day crawling on my gut to get to the work area.

MAY 8, 1959

Metal dust so thick, I need to wipe my goggles constantly. Had a coughing jag today. Don't think those masks are worth a damn sometimes. Compartment is so hot; I'm sweating like a pig. I strip as soon as I get home. Pam says no matter how much she washes my clothes they still smell of metal. Kids were waiting for me with shouts of 'Happy Birthday, Daddy.' Makes it all worth it.

MAY 8, 1959

I waited on the front stoop for Daddy to come home tonight. It's his birthday. We made a chocolate cake for him and had his presents all wrapped. Daddy loved the two Louis L'Amour westerns and the blue shirt. He said he'd wear his new shirt on Sunday to church. We ate dinner a little late because he soaked for so long in the tub first. And then he wanted his usual foot rub. Jean and I do it together, but Jean is the best. Daddy says she should be a nurse. She has the "magic touch." I use tweezers to try to get the metal slivers out of his feet. Even with big thick work boots, his feet are full of them. He says it's from the grinding on the welds. I got some of the slivers out, but most are tiny and stay stuck in his skin. I wonder, does it go through his mask too? Is that why he coughs so much?

MAY 10, 1959

Saw my brother Joe leaving the yard today. The whistle had just blown, and he was in his usual rush to get to the nearest bar. The guys don't have far to go. If you wait a couple of hours most of them will be staggering up the hill. There must be ten bars across from the shipyard. My van driver only takes guys ready to pull out right at four. Suits me fine. Wife and kids don't need a guzzled paycheck.

MAY *11, 1959*

I'm worried about Daddy. I got up to go to the bathroom last night and saw him slumped over the back of a chair in the kitchen. He does that when he has trouble breathing. I asked Mom if I could help. She told me to go back to bed. Daddy was just having one of
his bad spells. I heard his driver honk for him this morning at 6:30. I peeked out my bedroom window, and saw him going out the front door, carrying his black metal lunchbox. I hope Mom packed him something good today.

MAY *11, 1959*

Pirelli did his rounds today. He's not the worst pipefitter inspector, but you only hear from him when you've screwed up. So far, every one of my jobs has been clean. I take some pride in that. Got word today that they want us to work overtime this weekend, both Saturday and Sunday. Have to take it. Overtime pay is too good to pass up. Hope I manage to see some of Danny's game Saturday after work. Tried pitching a few balls to him after supper tonight. The boy has a good swing and could have played longer, but my arm felt like a dead weight.

MAY *14, 1959*

We went to church without Daddy. It didn't seem the same. Mom's been pretty quiet all morning, although we did have our bacon and egg breakfast. We didn't stop for donuts though. Daddy always does that after church on Sunday morning. I missed him reading us the funny papers. He worked yesterday too. Jean and I rubbed his feet again, and he fell asleep even while we were doing it. He must have been really tired.

MAY *18, 1959*

Ate lunch with Ed Marschett today. He's just been moved to our area. He's telling me that some of the guys have heard that the asbestos insulation used in the ship is toxic. Hell, they've used that stuff in all my work areas. Marschett told me he'd keep me posted if he hears anything else. Pam gave me a nice change from the bologna and cheese today. Real roast beef! And a little love note packed in with the cookies.

MAY 25, 1959

I hate it when Mom and Dad fight. Mom was upset that Daddy has to work overtime again this weekend. He yelled, "The bills have to be paid, and what do you mean there isn't enough for the electricity bill?" Mom had to remind him about the medicine she picked up for his asthma and the dental visits, and that two of the kids had cavities. I'm going to brush my teeth extra from now on.

MAY 29, 1959

The yard is getting all spruced up this week. They are getting ready for the big show. The USS George Washington will be launched in a little over a week. She's a pretty impressive sight. Got the specs on her today. Over 380 feet long, weighing 5,959 tons. After the launch she'll sail to Florida to be outfitted with the Polaris missiles. We'll be lucky if we see much of the launch. So much security, media, and big whigs around. Our assigned viewing area is pretty far away.

JUNE 7, 1959

Word out on the yard is that after the launch there may be layoffs. I guess I won't tell Pam until I know for sure. No sense worrying her. Last layoff lasted six weeks. Kids were eating sugar sandwiches for lunch. Pam spent every Saturday morning mixing up dried milk for the week. Wish we could manage to put some money away, maybe enough to buy a house; no more threats from the landlord. But it never seems to happen.

JUNE 9, 1959

I watched the news with Daddy on TV tonight. They showed the launching of the submarine that he's been working on. I looked really hard to see if they would show my Daddy. There was some lady hitting the hull of the sub with a bottle of champagne. Daddy says they do that with all the submarines. There were lots of men in uniforms, and a band playing. I didn't see Daddy anywhere. He said he was way in the back with the other workers. I think they should have all the workers up front. Maybe they could get a ribbon or something for all the work they did. Daddy fell asleep in his chair watching television. I heard him wheezing last night. I think he had another one of his "bad spells."

JUNE 11, 1959

The rumors about a layoff were wrong. The truth is worse. Joe's a union rep and he said contract negotiations are stalled. If the company doesn't counter with at least some pay increase and benefits, we'll be on strike. Hell, I only get one week paid vacation! Would sure love another week, but a strike? It means no unemployment checks and who knows how long it will last. I better keep taking those overtime hours no matter how much it takes out of me.

JUNE 14, 1959

School is out for the summer! Yeah! We begged Daddy to take us to the beach this weekend but he said he has to work both days. He never seems to laugh any more, like he used to. He did tell me he was proud of me when I showed him my report card. Said he bet I was the only fourth grader that got all A's. (I didn't tell him that Adam Kyenski also got straight A's, but everyone knows he's a genius.) Last time I got straight A's we went out for ice cream. Not this time.

JUNE 29, 1959

It happened, just like Joe said it would. Officially on strike. Great birthday present for my wife. She'll scrimp and pinch pennies like she always does, but it won't be enough. She wants to look for a job, but who would take care of the kids? The twins are still in diapers for Christ's sake. Pam's busy enough with five kids. She's a great mother; I don't want to see her working while some stranger, who doesn't even know or care about our kids, takes our money.

JULY 5, 1959

Daddy explained to me about the strike, and that even though he's not going to work he has to leave the house every day to walk the picket line. A picket line is when the workers go to the shipyard but instead of working, they walk on the sidewalk with signs and no one goes into work until the company agrees to give them more pay. I asked Daddy to give me the name of his boss and I would write a letter to tell him how hard he works. Maybe that would help. My teacher told me that I am a very good writer. He just smiled and gave me a big hug.

JULY 8, 1959

Only the third day on the picket line and already my feet are killing me. Didn't help that it rained most of the day. Pam drew me a hot bath when I got home. Would love to skip the line tomorrow but we get $15 a day from the union. It's a pittance, but it's something.

And who knows? Maybe the bastards will give in, and it will all be worth it.

JULY 12, 1959

I've been trying to think of a way to make money. I did sell lemonade one day but didn't sell much. Not enough to help with bills and stuff. So, I went knocking on neighbors' doors to ask if any of them had chores for me to do. And guess what? I got a job! Mrs. Davis, the old lady on the corner, says if I clean her house every Saturday, she'll pay me $10! She says I'm kind of young, but I promised her I'd do a good job. Mommy says it's okay as long as I finish my chores at home before I go. My chores are to clean my bedroom and family bathroom, and iron the clothes. I don't mind cleaning, but I hate to iron!

JULY 18, 1959

Had to call the doctor in last night. Dr. Weiss is good about making house calls. Told me that I should quit my job; it was killing me - breathing in all that metal dust; said my lungs were damaged. My response:

"And do what, Doc? I don't even have a high school education. Who would hire me?" He shook his head, said it was a damn shame that I dropped out of high school, that I was a smart guy. I reminded him that there was a war on back then. He'd forgotten that I was in the Army and fought overseas. I sure haven't forgotten. Lost a lot of buddies over there. Then he said I should check into the hospital. That's not going to happen. So, he gave me cough syrup; pretty strong stuff, knocks me out. Pam set up the vaporizer, rubbed Vicks on my chest. I think I'm doing a little better today.

JULY 20, 1959

I like my cleaning job. I gave Mom the $10 and she cried. I asked her why she was crying, but she didn't answer. Daddy is back on the picket line. He's coughing a lot every day. Uncle Joe came by and said he thinks the strike will be over soon. I asked him if that meant that Daddy would be getting more money. He said, "We'll see, honey, we'll see."

AUGUST 1, 1959

The strike is over. I'm scheduled to go back to work on Monday. Not sure the slight increase in pay and one more sick day was worth the long stretch without a paycheck, the walks on the picket line, or the pneumonia that the doc says I've yet to shake.

AUGUST 3, 1959

Daddy went back to work today. I got up extra early so I could give him a big kiss goodbye. I thought he'd be happy but he didn't look too good. Mom says he should be in the hospital. I'll say a rosary tonight before bed that God will make him all better.

AUGUST 7, 1959

The doctor got his way. I'm in the hospital. I was doing grinding work in the midsection where the launch tubes are located. Tight quarters. Suddenly I blacked out. Thank goodness Ed was there and called for help. Didn't come to until they wheeled me out of the ambulance. How the hell am I going to pay for that ride? They've got me on oxygen. Maybe that will turn things around. Pam brought me my diary and rosary beads. Praying I can beat this.

AUGUST 7, 1959

Daddy is in the hospital! I wanted to go see him but Mom said I needed to stay home and take care of the kids. I fixed them hot dogs and beans for supper but I was too upset to eat. The twins are in their cribs, finally! They fussed for Mom and I had to read them about ten books before they fell asleep. Danny and Jean tried to wait up for Mom with me but Danny fell asleep on the couch after watching the Red Sox game and Jean crawled into Mommy and Daddy's bed. I checked on her a few minutes ago. She's curled around Dad's pillow. It's all wet from her tears. I'm trying not to cry.

AUGUST 9, 1959

The doctor isn't giving me great news. Says my lungs are damaged, which has put a strain on my heart. Said given my line of work, I might have something called mesothelioma. He's running tests. He won't say much more. Sleep only in spurts. Nurses coming and going, checking on the oxygen delivery and other tubes I've got stuck in me. I was afraid in Belgium, shivering in my foxhole and fighting the Nazis, but I was single then. If I got hit, I was just another GI whose number was up. This is different. I've got a family to support. They need me, dammit!

AUGUST 12, 1959

Mommy says we are all going to the hospital tonight to visit Daddy. Jean and I traced the twins' hands and helped them color it in for get well cards. She, Danny, and I each made a card too. Everyone is excited to see him. Maybe he'll be coming home soon!

AUGUST 12, 1959

I can barely lift up this pen to write. Tried not to choke up when the kids came to visit. God, they're all so dear to me! The doctor said I could take the oxygen mask off while they visited, but only briefly. How can I leave them behind? They wanted to know why I was crying, and I just told them it was because I love them all so much and miss them. It was a strain to talk. Pam said she'd be back in the morning, but I don't know if I'll still be here. Each breath hurts. They say that when you come close to death there's a bright white light. All I see is darkness.

AUGUST 13, 1959

Last night when we saw Daddy, he didn't look the same! His words scared me, like he was saying goodbye. He hugged me and said he loved me. Told me he was proud of me and that I need to keep helping Mommy with the kids, that he was counting on me to be strong. But his voice was so weak, and I could barely hear him. Before we left, he had to put this mask over his face so he could breathe. I don't feel very strong. When I got home, I crawled into bed, pulled the covers over my eyes, and held my breath. What is it like to not breathe? I wanted to know. But finally, I had to breathe. My head was hurting and the darkness scared me. Is Daddy scared too?

Theresa Schimmel is the author of two novels, *Braided Secrets* and *Yankee Girl in Dixie*. She has also published four children's books: *The Carousel Adventure, Sunny, The Circus Song,* and *David's War/David's Peace.* Her short stories and poems have been featured and won awards in literary magazines and newspapers. Her books can be found on her website: www.tamstales.net.

BLACKBIRDS

by Julie Yingling

While I waited for the coffeemaker to drip dark caffeine, I gazed out to the birdfeeders where a few blackbirds cackled, chasing away smaller wrens and sparrows. I frowned and continued to monitor them as I made my way, mug and phone in hand, to my reading chair. Mr. Darcy climbed into my lap, snuggled close to my belly. My fingers slid through his thick, silky coat.

Tick. Tock. I could not hear it yet, and only named it after the countdown reached zero, but even as we continued to wipe down groceries and accumulate masks, the clock of a more personal tragedy started ticking that day. Perhaps Mr. Darcy heard.

*

We had met long ago. Cal loved to tell the story of the two "first" dates. My first date ended at the student union where I, unnerved by his good looks, had spilled my Coke all over the table and us. Cal's first date was a party at his shared rental house where he invited me to stay overnight and I declined. Neither recalled the other's version of our "first" date. At the time, we each retreated from those awkward scenes to the comfortable college steadies we had taken breaks from. And didn't think much about each other until thirty years later when the alumni bulletin revealed that we both lived in California.

Will there be anything left of that first attraction?

I had doubts about my very old memory of sparks flying. But sure enough, they flew again when we met for brunch in Half Moon Bay. We had an ocean view and a waitress who was entranced that we were meeting again after so many years.

"You two stay as long as you like."

And so we did. We met again over crab omelets and unlimited mimosas.

"Do you like to travel?" I had to know; I loved to travel.

"Yes, I travel quite a bit."

"Do you like to cook?"

"I do cook."

"What did you have last night?"

"Grilled chicken and asparagus, salad."

Soon, we commuted 350 miles on weekends to see each other. Gradually I learned that the travel he mentioned was for work and he much preferred his own nest. And that his cooking was limited to salad and grilled meat. Still, we smiled more when we were together.

Right after I retired, I moved down the coast to Cal who lived in the mountains above Santa Cruz. I puttered about, faux-finishing his walls with paints in cloudy peach and calming teal and pale yellow. But I wished for a companion while Cal continued his long commute to work. After a local yoga class, another regular mentioned her new Maltese puppy to a fellow student and offered to show him. I sidled closer to their conversation at the entrance.

"May I see the puppy too? I am looking for a small dog."

"Sure. He's just outside in my truck. Dan at Puppy Love Kennels is a great guy and just over the hill from here."

Lydia's Frosty was a tiny snowball of energy with black button eyes. I called Dan who invited me to meet a litter of Lhasa apso pups he was expecting in a few days. My sister Anna, visiting for the winter holidays, agreed to go with me. As we walked toward the outdoor kennel, three fluffy little bodies bounced around playing tag and bumper-pups. When they spotted us, the first ran to hide behind the doghouse, the second gazed dreamily into space. The third locked eyes with me and walked forward. I sat on the ground, and he climbed into my lap.

"Looks like you've found your dog, Jen. Or he's found you," Anna observed.

On the way home, we considered names from our favorite classics.

"Heathcliff?" offered Anna.

"Nah, too dark and brooding."

"What about Mr. Darcy?"

We searched for confirmation in this quiet and alert puppy, with a long silky white coat and black-tipped ears.

"Perfect!"

Cal was completing his engineering career, commuting fifty miles a day, and gardening in the few remaining hours. He was tired yet could not imagine what his life would be without work.

"I'm not sure I want a dog. It'll take a lot of energy and time." His face contracted.

"Really? Well, I'll do the work, and I have the time."

Within days, Cal was playing with the puppy and planning the dog door.

Mr. Darcy and I attended puppy school, played in the back garden, and walked the hilly neighborhood. He was tiny and needed protection more than once. The first threat was a huge German shepherd that charged from a backyard and barked ferociously; I stepped between the two dogs and yelled no! while I waved my arms madly over my head. Crazy dog stopped. As this registered, I remembered to breathe. Later, two coyotes tracked us from the brush beside the road. I again placed myself closest to the threat and we picked up our pace.

Early in his first year, I sat on the ground in the garden in front of a stone wall while the puppy ran around me, playing keep-away. On the third circle, he ran around behind my back and failed to reappear. I turned to find that he had banged his head into the rock wall. He could not keep his head up; it drooped on his neck like a broken flower.

Although he recovered, in the course of his care we discovered he had a blood clotting disorder. Every now and then, he would take a tumble, or his rottweiler friend Riley would race across a field to greet him and crash into him hard. Then he'd raise a puffy hematoma that lasted a week or more. We worried, but he learned to be more careful and to warn other dogs with a sharp bark to stay civil. Most of the time it worked.

*

"My back has been aching and now I see blood in my urine. What do you think it is?"

"I have no idea, but I would see a doctor if I were you."

We were one year out from the 2016 election. I had inured myself to the national news, but this very personal news startled me. After many tests, Cal was diagnosed with an aggressive form of cancer. We examined the research comparing radical surgery with chemo and radiation. He began chemotherapy infusions. When he was within two sessions of the recommended course of treatment, he called me one morning from our bed.

"I feel like I'm dying."

"You don't look good at all. I'm getting my phone."

Cal's skin was gray, his head was bald, and he could barely move. At the cancer center, they filled him with magnesium and fluids. When we returned home, he crawled into bed. Mr. Darcy followed. Until he was ready to start radiation, he was in bed quite a lot and Mr. Darcy was by his side much of the time.

Although Cal's cancer gave me a lot to do with my days, it also increased my sense of something very wrong in my world. The color faded. But as the next election approached and Cal's health returned, so did hope. And a tint of rose returned to my life. My step quickened and Mr. Darcy stepped along with me.

Then, the news of a new and very contagious virus hit. When the lockdown began, we followed all the rules and became more isolated.

I was frustrated by the lack of solid information or even comforting words at the national level. Cal seemed unconcerned.

A plague. And the worst president I can recall. What is that annoying ticking sound?

I sighed, signaled to Mr. Darcy, and grabbed the leash as I often did when stumped by an intractable problem. The ticking was audible now, but our footsteps in fallen leaves could still mask the sound.

In lockdown, the color that had started to return ebbed away again, followed by a feeling that none of it was real. Even when meeting friends for coffee, bundled up at outdoor cafes, life was like watching an old television show with colorless, pleasant characters. Ozzie and Harriet. Black and white and bland. Except for Mr. Darcy. He was always in full color: gold and cream and black with pink paws.

This ticking is getting worse. I'm afraid to get my hearing tested; it could be something psychological.

"Do you want chicken or fish for dinner?"

"Either. Doesn't matter."

During the pandemic's relative isolation, Mr. Darcy's quiet attention helped fill the gaps left by the uneasy silences between Cal and me. Cal was his daily playmate again, now that his treatments were done and his cancer was gone. And at night Mr. D. snuggled with me, waiting to see the occasional dog on TV.

He was fifteen years old when, one Sunday at the end of the first lockdown summer, Mr. Darcy leapt off the deck to chase a squirrel. For the rest of the day, he moved slowly, ignored the chipmunks, and avoided the stairs.

"We should call the vet in the morning." Cal said, his brow crinkled in concern for his companion.

That evening when I was on a Zoom call with my brothers and sisters, Mr. Darcy sat down before me and looked into my eyes. I picked him up and he lay still in my lap throughout the call. But he did not follow us to the bedroom later. Early in the morning, after being half-awake listening for him through the night, there was a thump.

I should never have left him alone.

I ran into the living room, Cal just behind me, where Mr. Darcy was lying on his stomach, breathing fast and shallow, eyes closed. I knew there was little to be done for the internal bleeding that was finally too much. I knelt beside him, my hands resting lightly on his back, praying he wasn't in pain. Cal was distraught. We both knew. The ticking was deafening now.

"Don't go, Darcy." Cal sobbed.

"He's dying, Cal." I said softly.

Mr. Darcy opened his eyes, rose slightly on his front paws, looked at me, and barked once. He dropped again and was gone.

The ticking . . . It stopped.

My hand lingered a beat on Cal's arm on my way to the window. My sight was blurred, but clear enough to see perhaps forty blackbirds in the trees and on the ground. I'd never seen so many at once.

A murmuration.

They began to stir as one and wheeled away into the brightening pink sky.

Julie Yingling is a retired academic who specialized in communication development and taught in California, Colorado, Iowa and Wisconsin. She now lives in South County with her husband and dog where she paints, gardens, and happily writes about whatever strikes her fancy.

DO NOT GO GENTLE

by Eric Crook

Everything I needed to know came across in the tone of her voice. It was midday when I was distracted by insistent beeping from my cell phone. I glanced down and saw the name "Brianna" pop up on the screen. It was two hours earlier in Tucson, so she should be at the hospital visiting my Uncle Jay. Brianna is the home health aide I've hired to assist my 91-year-old uncle in his final months.

"I'm with Jay, he just told me he is ready to die. He said he's comfortable with it." Brianna spoke these words firmly, but with deep and abiding compassion. I also caught the hesitation in her voice. These were painful words that she had had to say to dozens of relatives, friends, and executors for the deceased on all too many occasions. It was just part of her job. In the month or so we had been working together, I had come to trust her judgment without the slightest reservation.

In truth, I was hoping for a better outcome. In the two years since I had accepted the obligation of being my uncle's executor, there had been several close calls. But I was always holding out for one more reprieve. We often refuse to acknowledge when the end is nigh, even when that harsh reality is staring us in the face. I was no different.

We continued the conversation. We talked about how inadequate his treatment at St. Mary's Hospital had been. We expressed hopes that he might still make it into the rehab facility near my parents, thirty minutes south in Green Valley. But now, given his pronouncement that morning, I doubted that this would ever be the case. Throughout his entire life, when my uncle made a decision there was no equivocation; he was stubborn and strong-willed. It was this determination that drove him to a life of stunning accomplishments and fostered the deep love and admiration that my entire family held for him. When we ended the call, I was fighting back tears.

Uncle Jay was an all-powerful role model to my brother Keith, my sister Kathy, and myself. When we were growing up, no one ever went anywhere. But Jay went everyplace. After two years in the service, he went to Pakistan to study, got his bachelor's degree from the University of Dacca and converted to Islam. While there, he was almost corralled into an arranged marriage with a beautiful Bengali girl. But as fate would have it, he was expelled from Pakistan for unwittingly shaking hands with a man who turned out to be a government opposition leader. Or so, that's the way Jay told it.

When JFK announced a bold new foreign policy initiative hallmarked by the establishment of the Peace Corps, Uncle Jay was quick to join. After that, the details have always been unclear as to exactly what happened and when. We kids have debated these points - ad infinitum. At times our competing theories would rise to the level of an Indiana Jones saga; such is the blending of myth and history. During his years with the Peace Corps, it was clear he was given a wide range of assignments. Every year he would return home for the holidays and treat us to slide shows depicting the exotic places he had visited and worked. We were shown photographs of farm fields being tilled in Pakistan, rivers flooding in India, villages carved out of cliffs in Turkey, all the way to pictures of Jay riding an Egyptian camel in front of the Pyramid of Cheops. And it can be stated definitively that he spent at least two years in Iran as the Peace Corps' Deputy Director.

Jay left the Peace Corps during the Nixon administration. He continued to live in Tehran, working for a time in private industry before he attended the University of Tehran. There he taught foreign languages (he spoke at least a dozen fluently and numerous dialects as well) while he pursued a doctorate in Comparative Religion. He was teaching and writing his dissertation in early November of 1979 when some radical students stormed the U.S. Embassy and took 66 hostages.

Several weeks into the crisis, a less militant contingent from amongst the hostage-takers approached him and asked for his advice. As Jay described the discussion, he first told them that it would never end well, and they should let everyone go. When his advice fell on deaf ears, he then suggested that they should at least let the office workers, who were the women and the Blacks, go free, since they certainly had done nothing wrong. Then, evidently persuaded by Jay's argument, on November 19 and 20, thirteen hostages were set free. Eleven were women and two were Black. Jay's role in their release has never been a matter of public record. The crisis continued for 444 days and has had severe repercussions on U.S. relations with Middle Eastern countries that still haunt us today.

Jay often told us that he had been kicked out of three countries: Pakistan, as has been mentioned, Yemen, where he was suspected of being a CIA agent (not the first time that had happened) and was held at gunpoint before being expelled, and Iran. But his departure from Iran is a story full of conjecture. He managed to stay in Iran for about nine months after the hostages were taken. He continued working at the university, completed and successfully defended his thesis, and received a Ph.D for his efforts. He stated that he was generally left alone to go about his business in a society where one's faith stands above allegiances and nationality.

But he did admit to me that he had often been hassled in the streets and taken to the local police. Fortunately, he had good friends at the precinct and things never went beyond that. His ace in the hole, it would appear, was that Jay was widely known to be a fierce critic of the Shah. Still, I am certain that during those months he was constantly being followed. So then, how did he make his escape?

As my sister Kathy remembers it, he simply flew home, and my dad, with my very relieved grandmother, picked him up at JFK airport. But years ago, I pointedly asked him how he got out of Iran, and he replied simply, "By bus." I also recall he mentioned passing through Tabriz, which is 390 miles northwest of Tehran. For both of these explanations to ring true, my uncle must have taken local buses to Tabriz, and then continued in the same fashion for another 166 miles to the Turkish border. From there he could easily make arrangements to fly home via Ankara or Istanbul.

My brother Keith and I started clearing out Jay's house four days after his passing. There was no question of keeping it; Jay often claimed that he had lived twelve years longer than he had expected. As such, he hadn't done any real maintenance for at least that long. So, between sleeping in Jay's bedroom, which was inundated with mold, or using the same hospital bed where Jay had breathed his last, Keith chose the living room. I slept with the mold.

Each morning began with instant coffee and whatever we managed to scrape together for breakfast. Then we'd decide who would work in what room and on which set of bookcases. As the executor, the task of examining and sorting legal papers, correspondence, and account statements fell to me. Beyond the occasional revelation about Jay's life revealed in his personal effects, there was no joy for either of us, but it had to be done. The third day we hopped into the van and brought 40 boxes of books and 15 boxes of CDs (all classical music) to St. Vincent de Paul. When we got back to the house we looked around, stunned by the enormity of the task. We hadn't made the slightest dent in the mess. When a dumpster finally arrived, we threw bags and boxes of garbage into it, filling it in less than two hours.

We arranged for a family gathering a week later at the Marana Mortuary, only six miles from where Jay would be interred nine days later. I figured on an hour for the service and then a luncheon at a splendid Persian restaurant that Keith had found. We began with a traditional ceremony at the end of which my father stood up and received the stars and stripes from a young officer in dress uniform. After taps was played, I made a brief introduction. Friends and family expressed their remembrances of how brilliant and loving Jay was. He was simply a fascinating character. My wife had arrived the day before the memorial, and we stayed at a resort for the four days she was visiting.

That night after the family gathering, she and I lounged in a Jacuzzi, watching fleecy clouds race past a full moon. It was a brief respite from the madness. The preceding days had been a mélange of overwhelming grief, resolute determination, and petty disputes. Here, finally in the moment with Joanne by my side, I felt restored. In the morning we went out early and had breakfast before I took her to the airport. The following day my brother flew back to Connecticut. I was alone.

Over the 18 days it took to prepare his estate to be liquidated, I spent countless hours circumnavigating Tucson in an ungainly van and then, thankfully, for the last week in a far more comfortable SUV. It was a dusty city; it struck me as a poor town with a big college. I drove through the city center, the suburbs, and the periphery. I was struck by how much Tucson resembled the slides of Tehran that Jay had shown us years ago - another dusty place surrounded by treeless mountains. As best as I could figure, Jay spent more days of his life living in Tucson than any other place on earth. Though there were plenty of industries supported by freight rail lines surrounding the city, they didn't look like high-end purveyors of well-paying jobs. The bars looked seedy, and the restaurants did not impress.

Windstorms were kicking up across the desert chapparal the day I drove from Tucson to the storage units I had rented near my parents' home in Green Valley. The van I was using negotiated the gusty winds like a fish, its backend swishing back and forth. I had decided to combine Jay's writings with other important family heirlooms. These included over 250 of my father's paintings. He had been renting the unit for years and had never bothered to check how things were holding up. When I rolled up the door what I found looked like a photograph of a Pharoah's tomb. Pictures were knocked akilter and everything was layered in dust. I cleaned it up and made room for Jay's stuff. It seemed like the best solution.

The next day, I worked with a crew I had hired and carted the last 106 boxes of Jay's books off to Goodwill. Then they, too, bid me farewell. I returned to the empty adobe stucco home where Jay had resided for so many years and was overcome by the finality of that moment. I curled up on his couch, the only stick of furniture left in the house, hugging my knees against my chest. I felt like a thief. I had stolen a man's life, a man I had always loved and admired, a man who was also loved and admired by everyone in my circle. And I had knowingly, deliberately, scattered his possessions hither and yon. I thought of the uniqueness of his life and suffered the pain of having to accept that everything I cherished most about Jay was now only memories.

My preference was to read the famous, fixed-verse villanelle composed by Dylan Thomas in 1947, purportedly written as a tribute to his dying father. But I had to admit, if only to myself, that honoring my uncle's religious beliefs was as much my duty as it was being there at graveside to see that he was properly put to rest. So, I found myself at dawn on Valentine's Day sitting on Jay's couch, reading the Koran. It was a beautiful, leather-bound, three-volume set in Arabic with side-by-side English translations. As I read through it, I was struck by how much the text seemed no different than that of the Bible. There were no screeds about terrorism and jihad, at least in the sections I read.

But then this was fundamental to what made Jay the man that he was: he was a contrarian about everything. He did not accept the religion most common to his birthright. He always seemed to be striving to find something deeper, something mysterious, something that could be felt but not known. So, during the Iranian Revolution he wrote his doctoral thesis on the similarities between the parables of the Koran and the stories of the Bible, and then published six more books on the subject. Whether you agreed with his ideas or not, he was a brilliant, caring man who always seemed to be searching for ways to lessen conflict in human relations. I chose two passages from the Koran that I thought he would like to hear and drove up north to the Veterans Cemetery in Marana.

The sky was an amazing blue, almost ethereal in its intensity. The wind was brisk, but fortunately died down just as the casket was transported to the grave. The haunting notes of taps rang out and as soon as the trumpeter finished, I began. First, I read a passage that described the Islamic version of Genesis: the majesty of the universe borne out of darkness. This I followed with a passage from Chapter 23 (The Believers):

In the name of God, The Merciful, The Compassionate, Surely the ones who believe have prospered, those, they who in their formal prayers *are* ones who are humble ... Truly they *are* ones who are irreproachable ... And those, they who their trusts and their compacts *are* ones who shepherd and those, they who over their formal prayers *are* watchful. Those, they *are* ones who will inherit, those who will inherit Paradise, they *are* the ones who will dwell in it forever.

And with that it was done, and my uncle was lowered into the ground. For all the love, for all the sorrow, for all the wonder this universe can provide, I hope he has found what he's always been searching for. *Inshallah*.

Eric Crook is a regular contributor to the ARIA Anthology. He is a versatile writer whose contributions have ranged from poetry to light fiction, essays on environmental issues and here a story that is deeply personal. At this moment he is working on a sequel to his first novel, which will be titled "A Thing as Lovely . . . ."

THE MIDNIGHT CAROUSEL

by Victor Contente

A blood orange sun fell over Narragansett Bay in Riverside, Rhode Island. The sunset sky was painted in splashes of purplish-pink, turquoise, and lemony-lime tangerine. Spilling out from the bay, the ice-glazed Providence River glistened in the darkness like a Del's frozen cherry lemonade. Overlooking the river, Crescent Park was shrouded in a supernatural crimson haze.

In the velvety dusk, an American bald eagle soared high over the park and hunted for carrion, but it flew too close to a bird rookery and was attacked by a murder of black crows. The territorial crows defended their nests with vigor by dive-bombing and pecking at the lone eagle from different directions. Bloody and battered, dizzy and disoriented, the eagle spiraled down to the winter wonderland below, ricocheted off the clam shack, and parachuted onto a pile of snow near the Crescent Park carousel.

A severe arctic chill gripped all of Riverside. The silent church bells at St. Brendan's were frozen in place by thick ice. Coast Guard cutters, cargo barges, and supertankers no longer headed out to the bay. Despite the frigid winter blast, Otis Washington was covered in a blanket of sweat and deep asleep in his Crescent Park bed. The ex-Marine held his bloody service dog Huey protectively under both of his prosthetic arms. Transported in his sleep thousands of miles away, Otis again fought for his country in the napalm-laced hellholes of Vietnam.

A monsoon of orange acid rain pelted Otis as he struggled to catch his breath in the suffocating heat and humidity. The lone soldier was lost and trapped behind enemy lines. In a succession of synchronized attacks, the Marine was eaten alive by malarial mosquitoes, blood-sucking leeches, and red fire ants. Venomous snakes, hidden booby traps, and explosive land mines were scattered everywhere on the battlefield. Otis was surrounded by Vietcong guerillas, who camouflaged themselves in the dense jungles and foliage, and fired at him from every direction. God was missing in action, thought Otis, but he refused to lose hope and faith in his mission. In the distance he heard the rhythmic, comforting sounds of the approaching rescue helicopters. Otis let out a sigh of relief and an "Oorah," just moments before he was greeted by the hand grenade that shattered his world to pieces.

The embattled soldier violently tossed and turned in his sleep to flee the horrors of Vietnam. Huey barked and did his best to wake up Otis. A compassionate blast of thunder jolted the park and Otis was transported back to his Riverside battlefield. The startled veteran rolled off his moldy park bench with Huey still in his arms, and together the two comrades crashed onto a minefield of broken Narragansett beer bottles.

Otis's living carcass was comfortably numb, thanks to a generous cocktail of pain pills and beer. His yellow diabetic toes were nearly frostbitten in his worn-out and soleless combat boots. To keep his bald head warm and dry he donned an honorary Vietnam Veteran cap, and he was always faithfully dressed in his original battlefield fatigues. He wore a pirate patch over his blind right eye. The irreversible spread of Agent Orange ate away at the black skin on his face and body. His rotting but still breathing corpse reeked of putrid body odor and skunk-smelling medicinal weed. Narragansett beer infiltrated his bloodstream and oozed from his pores.

Otis struggled to thaw open his frozen eyelids and, despite the thick shroud of fog that always engulfed him, he spotted the glowing specter of a mysterious woman hovering by the Providence River. She wore a black veiled hat, a scarlet Victorian dress, and stylish boots. The dark lady gazed out toward the bay and repeatedly called out the name William, but there was no response, only a deafening silence. Otis was spellbound by the ghostly lady and deep inside his broken heart he felt her private pain. He shouted out a kind hello to the woman in distress. She slowly turned toward Otis and looked compassionately at the unresponsive Huey. Her skin was phantom blue, some of her bones were exposed, and the eyes on her ashen face were a radiant green. Otis was not frightened. Vietnam had hardened him; he had seen the best of the worst in the world, and nothing shocked him anymore. Instead, he was drawn to her commitment and strength. She was hauntingly beautiful and carried herself with the admirable grace and determination of someone who refused to be defeated.

Deafening booms of thunder rocked Riverside and fast-flickering flashes of lightning lit up the park like a Bristol Fourth of July fireworks celebration. Otis picked up Huey in his arms and instinctively ducked for cover. His heart thumped like a military helicopter in his chest. Otis felt like everything inside of him had suddenly short-circuited. The earth appeared to have stopped spinning and life appeared to be frozen in time. In the blink of one bloodshot eye, the artillery of lightning ceased and Crescent Park was magically transported back to another dimension in time. Gone was the winter of darkness and despair, replaced by the sunny promise of warmth and hope. The bright sky was lightly tinted in a mystic powder blue. Chirping red cardinals danced in the fresh air as they flew between the flowering shade trees. Playful squirrels feasted on abundant acorns and scurried around in the lush green grass. The shining waterway bustled with riverboats and cargo ships, and trollies full of excited visitors poured in and out of the park.

Men and women were dressed in their Sunday best. The men wore top hats and tweed suits, while the women wore fashionable hats and long Victorian-style dresses. They dined at the shore dinner restaurant and waltzed in the spacious dance hall. Girls wore pretty summer dresses and boys were clad in knickerbocker pants with suspenders. Boys swam in the river and fished off the pier. Girls played Skee-Ball at the penny arcade and read books in the pastoral shade. Adults and children rode the Flying Toboggan roller coaster and the majestic Crescent Park carousel. Food stands sprouted everywhere and sold delicious French fries, mouthwatering cotton candy, and fresh popcorn. There was something for everyone at the fair. It was a grand carnival filled with endless fun, laughter, and excitement.

The lady in dark was on a search mission, and she pushed her way through the swarming crowd of revelers and stopped to ask a group of young boys if they had seen her lost son William. Yes, they replied, they spent most of the morning fishing and swimming with William, and later they all met up again at the carousel and rode the merry-go-round. This, they said, was the last time they saw William, who chose to remain at the carousel after the boys left. As the desperate woman pondered their words, an army of black clouds snuffed out the sun and the once-bright sky grew eerily dark. A powerful bolt of lightning struck a building up near Bullocks Point Avenue. Horror flashed across the distraught mother's face when she noticed that the carousel was engulfed in flames. Screams filled the park, and stampedes of panic-stricken parents rushed toward the fire. Crescent Park was transformed into a chaotic battlefield. Perhaps it was due to his PTSD, or an overdose of painkillers, but Otis fainted and fell on a steaming pile of horse manure. Only the loyal Huey remained at his side.

When Otis regained consciousness, he was lying in a pile of snow like a fallen snow angel with broken wings. Gone was the merry amusement park, the rollicking roller coaster, and the penny arcade. The carousel was cloaked in darkness and the cheerful organ music no longer filled the air. There was no trace of the finely dressed men and women or of the happy children. Everyone, including the dark lady, had vanished into the thick fog. Otis's military shirt had been carefully placed on his body like a shroud. A bloody trail of three paw prints led out to the carousel. Huey had disappeared into the night.

Dead sober and painfully alive, Otis looked up to an indifferent heaven and prayed to his invisible God for Huey's return. In many ways, the stray yellow Labrador retriever was his soulmate - an aging, courageous, and handicapped dog who never stopped fighting. Only yesterday they scavenged for food together in the trash cans and dumpsters near the Honey Dew Donuts shop. Huey found a bag of jelly donuts in a tipped-over trash can. The happy dog wagged his tail as he carried his proud bounty to his master across the street. Neither one of them saw or heard the speeding green Jeep as it slid on the black ice and swerved toward the dog. The sound of screeching tires was followed by a painful yelp. As the drunk driver sped away, Otis picked up his wounded dog like a fallen comrade, flipped him over his shoulder, and carried him back to the sanctuary of their park bench. Huey was in shock and one of his paws was bleeding profusely. Otis unbuttoned the shirt of his military uniform and wrapped it around his injured dog's paw. Sitting half-naked on the frosty park bench with Huey in his arms, Otis consoled his friend as he heard the comforting sound of the approaching rescue helicopters.

"Here they come, Huey! Hang in there, old bud, the Marines never leave anyone behind."

Otis fought back tears as he gazed up at the vast galaxy, and saw a shooting star. Smoking his medicinal weed, Otis wondered if he would be any less invisible, any less misunderstood, any less discriminated against, and any less lonely living on Pluto. Yes, he thought, Pluto would be the perfect home for him: a misunderstood place in the universe that was once thought to be a planet, but then reclassified and eventually erased as a planet. He would definitely feel at home there. Once a decorated Purple Heart war hero, Otis was also misunderstood, reclassified as just another homeless bum, and eventually erased as a true human being. As he took another deep puff, he reflected on how he had become an alien on his own planet, just another stray animal fighting to survive. Hell, he thought, even the ferocious lions and tigers at the Roger Williams Park Zoo are regularly fed and live in warm shelters during the winter.

Otis tried not to shiver and surrender to the bitter cold. He was mentally drained and physically fatigued. He held his dear Huey closely to his chest and dozed off. As heavy snowflakes fell on Crescent Park,

Otis was transported from one storm and battlefield to another, and soon he found himself in the fiery purgatory of Vietnam.

Otis was in a state of shock. Fellow soldier Lance Lincoln picked up his fallen comrade from a swamp of blood and tossed him carefully over his broad shoulder. Lance dodged several rounds of enemy fire as he made his way to the rescue helicopter. Inside the weary medics worked feverishly on Otis to prevent him from being reclassified as another war casualty, another brave Marine sent home in a body bag. As the bloody helicopter rose to the sky like a fiery phoenix from the ashes, Lance consoled Otis with a healthy dose of military optimism. "Hang in there, my brother, you're going to be okay, we Marines never leave anyone behind."

When Otis awoke and returned to his Riverside battlefield, he was shrouded by the silhouette of the dark lady standing over him. Her haunting voice was calm, her reassuring tone was soothing, but her cryptic message was filled with a sense of urgency.

"Come, it is time for us to go. I found my son William at the carousel. I saw your dog limping slowly up the hill toward the street. Hopefully you will find your dog on the way." The phantom lady reached out her bony hand toward Otis and motioned for him to follow her as she floated up toward Bullocks Point Avenue. Otis was spellbound and he slowly crept up the frozen hill behind his ghostly partner. He was a wounded man who had lost everything and everyone, a man who was destroyed both physically and mentally, but he was also a victor and not a victim, a Marine fighter who refused to be defeated.

As Otis neared the brightly lit carousel, he heard the cheerful organ music and the gay laughter of children inside. He flashed back to his youth and the bright Sunday afternoons when his dear Aunt Teresa would bring him and his cousins Charlie and Stella to Crescent Park. These were the happiest memories of his life. It never occurred to him then during those bright and happy summers, that half a century later he would be at the carousel again, but this time knocking at death's door in the darkest winter of his life.

Otis stood at the threshold to the carousel. From there he saw the spirited children laughing merrily as they reached for the elusive brass rings. The colorful wooden horses they rode on appeared to be galloping in midair to the beat of the lively organ. Seated together on a chair of the carousel was the dark lady with her son William in her arms. William had a big smile on his face as he licked a chocolate ice cream cone. The phantom woman winked at Otis and motioned for him to join them. Several other midnight riders also called out to Otis. A surging warmth of unconditional love and a feeling of widespread acceptance filled the soldier's empty soul. At that shining moment he thought he had finally reached his paradise, his reward for all the sacrifices he had made and all hardships that he had faced on the countless battlefields of his life. Otis was overcome with tears and happiness. Perhaps God had not forgotten him.

Suddenly the carousel halted to a dead stop. The bright lights of the merry-go-round flickered wildly, and the happy organ music died along with the laughter. The startled horses grinned eerily. Fiery sparks flew from their mouths, and some of the trotters displayed their fangs. The children screamed in horror. The carousel was filled with an ambiance of fear and impending doom.

Still standing at the entrance door of the carousel, Otis thought he heard a dog barking outside. He felt his body short-circuit and he was lost in a battlefield deep within his tortured mind. Only the thunderous sound of the approaching rescue helicopters snapped him out of his trance. Through the deep fog outside he saw Lance motion him down the hill. He faithfully followed his comrade until they reached the helicopter. A crew of medics stood at the door of the helicopter and one of them released the barking dog. It was Huey! The happy dog wagged his tail as he ran toward his master. He was no longer bleeding, and he jumped in Otis's arms and licked his face. Lance and the medics saluted Otis before boarding the helicopter and disappearing into the misty sky.

Otis was exhausted but exhilarated from what had just transpired. He plopped down on his wobbly bed in the center of Crescent Park and, with Huey once again in his arms, he fell asleep and drifted off to a faraway land.

Vietnam was now a scenic paradise. Gone were the battlefields of Otis's past, replaced by the sublime beauty of misty limestone mountains, glistening rice fields, and enchanting waterfalls. He was welcomed with kindness by the Vietnamese people as he walked casually on a stunning beach with powdery white sand and clear turquoise water. Gone were the horrors of war, replaced by the serene tranquility of love and peace. Otis was overwhelmed. The hell he once knew as Vietnam was now a perfect slice of heaven on earth.

A hungry Huey licked Otis's face and woke him from his cathartic sleep. A new day was dawning. A bright lemony sun rose in a cloudless sky. The cold snap was broken and the snow was melting. Gone was the ice from the Providence River and a Coast Guard cutter rode the tranquil waves toward Narragansett Bay. The church bells of St. Brendan's rang in the distance. Sitting on the park bench with Otis and Huey was a huge white box neatly decorated with a purple bow. Inside the gift box were cozy blankets, countless gift cards to Honey Dew Donuts, several boxes of Milk Bones, and an enormous envelope stuffed with one-hundred-dollar bills. A handwritten note was also included in the package and it read, "Thank you for your service. Stay warm, eat well, and love your dog. See you soon, Angela."

Parked at the top of Bullocks Point Avenue was a green jeep. Inside sat a beautiful middle-aged woman. She beeped her horn, smiled, and waved at Otis and Huey, then drove off slowly. Near the Crescent Park carousel, a majestic American bald eagle rose from the snowy ashes, flapped its wings and soared up high into the welcoming sky.

Victor Contente recently joined ARIA's impressive group of local and talented authors. He enjoys writing dark and supernatural short stories and poems. He offers a special thanks to his wife Lucie (also an ARIA member) for her encouragement, and he hopes you enjoy reading "The Midnight Carousel" as much as he enjoyed writing it.

AMID DARK HEARTS

by Claremary Sweeney

I wonder how many shades of pale are hidden
 beneath those black balaclavas
Under cover of white sheets graying with use, fraying around eyeholes
Around mouth openings encrusted with yellowed spittle from filthy
 words spewed in rage
The rage of boys in the guise of men - grown children entitled
 to so much more
More than Jews or people with darker skins or women
 they fear will replace them?

I wonder if there is a hierarchy among you?
Are the whitest, the palest, the pearls among the swine revered?
Do they reign over the tanned, the freckled, the mottled,
 the blemished, the scarred?
But, then, you are all scarred
Isn't this what fuels your anger, your ire, your burning rage?

Scars and wounds handed down through generations
    of men to boys, boys to men
Ignorant, abusive men enabled by the silence of their women
Girls who cling to the ends of those white sheets
Mothers, sisters, wives, daughters
The Eva Brauns among us

I wonder what your meetings are like
Is the room redolent with the heat from your hostile bodies
    and the festering of your angry hearts?
Are your faces red with pent-up frustration, your fear,
    your hostility longing for release?
The release of marching together with burning torches
    and venomous chants,
A roomful of black hearts, of white fists thrust in the air

Heil!
Your flags unfurl
Segmented, coiled snakes on undulating backgrounds
    of green and white
"Don't Tread on Me!" "Join or Die!"
Just what will you do if I tread on you? If I choose not to join?

And so, I wonder how proud you really are as you hide
    under the cover of hoods
Is it safe under there?
Would you act so brave out in the open in a world
    repulsed by the hatred you spew?

Proud Boys, Cowboys, Mean Boys who are shackled
    by the weight of your pasts
Fractured men, tarnished souls seeking to find an exit from the cloth
    you've chosen to hide beneath.

We live in bleak times
In days blood-colored by your hatred and fear
A senseless hatred and fear of other people
Different people
For you "Hell is other people" not like you

Tangled in your robes
Smoldering under your hoods
Trying to break free from your pasts
From fathers who nurtured the hatred
From mothers who let them

And so, you remain caught beneath those robes
A cover for your anger, your hatred, your fears
Whatever will hide your past
And know that for you there will be no exit
No respite from the darkness of your hearts—

Claremary Sweeney is the author of *A Berkshire Tale and Carnivore Conundrum,* both
written for youngsters and those who are young at heart. Presently she is researching
and writing the seventh installment of the South County Mystery Series, books that
are centered around the historic villages and towns in southern Rhode Island.

BULLY

by Rick Billings

I t all came down to the shoes.

Like most of the kids in my neighborhood, I attended St. Mary's for lower and middle school. I am the youngest of four - my three sisters went through school before me. The upside for me was that my sisters were all very good students and generally kept out of trouble. Likewise, the downside for me was that my sisters were all very good students and generally kept out of trouble. I suppose I didn't realize it at the time, but apparently there was some sort of standard attached to me. Another looming factor was that my mom often drove the nuns to the market or to doctor or dentist appointments. With four kids going through the school, I think she earned some sort of tuition credit for toting them around. This gave her the inside track on our school activities as well.

From the first grade to the fourth or fifth, we were subject to the hard rule of the priests and nuns as was customary at a Catholic school in those days. I myself rarely bore the brunt of verbal or physical abuse at the hands (and sometimes feet) of angry, frustrated, repressed nuns, but I witnessed much of the same applied to others. We are now all aware of such conditions as dyslexia, attention deficit, obsessive natures, hyperactivity, and the like. In those early days of lower school, the kids, much like the nuns' habits, were simply looked at in a black and white way. Kids were viewed as either good or bad, smart or stupid, hard working or lazy, and were labeled as such. Indeed, the practice of turning your group of peers against you as a sort of pressure was commonplace. Often the entire class would be punished for one student's infraction. Curiously, this is also common practice in prisons and during military training. Consider the humiliation of having to sit in the wastebasket in front of your friends or having to wear the test marked with a failing grade pinned on your shirt for the day.

None of us would ever go home and complain that we were mistreated. It was accepted blindly by the parents that if you got into trouble with the nuns, there was a good reason for it. You would just get into more trouble at home for making the Sisters mad. Even in our own minds we never would have questioned being disciplined, given the implied respect we were expected to have for them from the start.

With all this, there were many positives at St. Mary's that my friends in public school didn't have. We certainly had more structure and discipline. We had classes not only in English, Math, Science, and (selective) History, but also Music and Art. They tried to give us a well-rounded education even if it was bracketed with the "Rule by fear" and "God is watching" templates.

How peculiar then that in the schoolyard there was little or no supervision at the start of the day.

Most days we grouped into playing basketball, handball, or some form of tag before the bell rang. In the fall, there were often "chestnut fights." Chestnut trees were all over the area at that time. (Several years later they succumbed to some sort of tree virus and the chestnuts were no more). We would trek up to Swan Point Cemetery with paper bags, enter through the rarely used South Path, throw sticks into the trees to knock the chestnuts down, then bring the bag full of the green pointy balls home to cut them open and release the beautifully deep, sienna-colored treasures inside. A hole was drilled through the larger, hefty specimens and a strong shoelace threaded through, double knotted at the end. In the schoolyard, you would challenge someone and face off.

Holding the nut between the index and middle finger you would snap it and hit your opponent's entry. Last chestnut standing wins. Somehow this frontier-style game endured in our schoolyard and after school gatherings despite the television boom that was sweeping the country.

St. Mary's schoolyard was a large, paved lot with four basketball courts at one side. There were two covered ramps leading into the building - one on each end. In the early days of the school, the ramps were used as separate entrances, marked "Boys" and "Girls." Those words were engraved in stone over the doors. When one of the Sisters came out and rang the handbell for the start of school or the end of recess, we lined up according to class on our respective side of the building. After running around like untethered maniacs, we were suddenly expected to stand quietly in line and march into the classrooms led by our teacher - no matter what had happened in the schoolyard.

Indeed, sometimes the atmosphere outside resembled a cross between Lord of the Flies and Thunderdome. Navy blue ties that were part of the boys' required uniform could quickly become a handle used to swing someone around by the neck. Boys with families of a lower income had the advantage here, as their cheaper clip-on ties popped right off in the aggressor's hand. Unfortunately, this usually fueled the initial anger further as laughter from the onlookers ensued and the clip-on wound up in a tree.

Another handy conversion was the girls' jump rope. The first infraction was to run by and steal the rope from the girls. The second infraction usually involved tying someone to the basketball post or the fence so that when the bell rang, they couldn't get into line. One rainy day as we all huddled in the shelter of the ramp, a few of the more aggressive older kids used a pilfered jump rope to bind the hands of John Norbitt (for some reason nicknamed "The Ferret" by the same boys) and hoist him up over a supporting bar for everyone to see, chanting "Stop the Ferret!" the whole time. That particular incident didn't go unnoticed. Everyone who was present on the ramp that day was brought in front of Monsignor Lloyd and Sister Edwardine to answer for what they'd done - or failed to do - in The Ferret's defense. To my knowledge, as was the custom in the day, no parents were informed of the incident by the school leaders or the students.

In another area of Pawtucket there was a school, called St. Maria Goretti, that the Catholic diocese decided to close. They farmed out the students to various other schools across the city. Two of those students landed in my classes. They were friends at St. Maria Goretti and came into St. Mary's at the same time. Some adult somewhere was thinking clearly and reasoned that the transition might be easier on the boys if they were transferred together. Kids at that age already have a kind of hierarchy among each other when they are in a group. It must be difficult to gain acceptance with a school full of kids who have been together since kindergarten.

Norman Beladeau was a gentle, low-key kid. Even at that age, I felt for him as I could see the nervous uncertainty on his face every day. He came to school in the proper uniform, stayed very quiet, and usually kept to himself. He appeared to have a gentle, kind, spirit. It seemed so odd that he was friends with the loud, brash, aggressive Richie Carpano. They resembled that cartoon pair of dogs, one a big tough bulldog, the other a small mongrel tagging along beside him.

Richie established himself early. He allied himself with the bigger, tougher kids and often preyed on the weaker and more vulnerable of us to get a laugh. I could see quickly what he was all about and tried my best to stay clear and off his radar. Sometimes though, despite your best efforts, trouble finds you just the same.

It all came down to the shoes.

For some reason that I still don't fully understand, I had a peculiar attachment to my shoes as a child. I recall having several pairs that I grew out of but kept wearing to the point of blisters rather than discarding them. My mother once had to retrieve a pair from the trash, after I cried when she threw them away. There was the brown leather pair that got a "grownup" polish on a Sunday morning from the shoeshine man during one of the few excursions when I was allowed to accompany my dad on his errands. There was the pair that we referred to as "Desert Boots" that I just couldn't let go of as well as numerous tattered sneakers that bore memories of summer.

My grandfather always had a good pair of shoes. In times when money was scarce, he always spent the extra for a better pair. He took care of them, too, always with a regular shine. Maybe I got it from watching him. A simpler explanation could be that money was just as scarce in our household and the pair of school shoes each year was one of the few things that I got absolutely new and actually had a say in. Clearly it was important to me in a way that I didn't see.

That particular year I had it in my head that I wanted a pair of shoes known as Alpine boots. I'd seen them somewhere around and just thought they were "the cat's pajamas" as my grandmother would say. They weren't in line with the school uniform, but St. Mary's gave a little wiggle room on footwear. They were a style similar to a hiking boot that was streamlined for everyday wear.

The place for our school shoes was the New York Lace Store down on Lonsdale Avenue. Mom took me there every year. She usually let me browse the display and pick a pair on my own. She would then bring one over to Mr. Anders and point him my way.

Mr. Anders was a tall, mostly bald, mid-40s man with the quiet tone and demeanor of a pediatrician. Whatever plan he had envisioned for himself, I'm sure it did not include looking at feet all day long and selling shoes in a department store. Yet he carried himself with dignity and confidence. He was polite and well-spoken and always wore a clean shirt and tie. He would greet my mom gently every time we were there. To me he would say, "Hello young man, how are you this afternoon?" Mr. Anders took pride in his work and followed through with the same professionalism that would have been expected of a banker or accountant. His service included that large silver medieval looking device that measured feet - the one that you always think is going to hurt but is really just very cold.

After taking the chosen shoe from my mom he would go into the back room (which I imagined to be a vast warehouse with impossibly high shelves that contained every style and size of shoe in existence) and come back out with my size as well as one size larger and one size smaller. He would remove each shoe from the box, thread the laces and exercise the leather, and then gently ease my foot into each shoe with the shoehorn that he produced seemingly out of thin air. The new shoes always had the fresh smell of shoe polish on leather. I love that new clean smell today as much as I did then.

Next I would walk around the shoe department. Mr. Anders would check my toe for proper fit, and if all was well we would be on our way. I still feel a great appreciation for the time and care that he spent to be sure that I had the right shoe.

In the particular year in question my mom agreed to buy me the Alpine boots that I was pining for. I was thrilled to leave the store with them. They were a rich, dark brown leather (like the color of the chestnuts) with a soft padded area around the ankle. Thick red laces crossed through copper-colored grommets from the hardshell toe to the top of the shoe. I thought they were beautiful.

Honestly, after wanting them so much, I found myself feeling very self-conscious as I walked to school. Those bright red laces really made them stand out. I was never one to want a lot of attention directed my way. I was just happy to have the shoes and the nice feeling that came with wearing them. Inevitably though, they were noticed just as soon as I walked into the schoolyard. Tony Neely walked up to me right away.

"Wow, those are nice! What kind of shoes are they?"

A few other kids gathered around as well. Soon we were in a little circle with a lot of chatter, while I kept trying to direct the conversation elsewhere.

"Where did you get them?"

"How much were they?"

"Is that real leather?"

"Do they have steel toes?"

Suddenly I heard a loud booming voice.

"Who's got steel toes?"

Richie Carpano came charging into the circle like a mad bull. He launched himself into the air and stomped down on my right shoe. Everyone scattered as I felt pain in my toes. When I looked down, there was a big dent in the toe of my beautiful new Alpine boot. I didn't have much time to react before the laughter started, led by Tony Neely of course. The humiliation of having this happen coupled with the knowledge that I was defenseless against Carpano and the laughter all around nearly brought me to tears. The only thing that kept me from crying was that I knew it would make the situation so much worse. I suddenly understood with full clarity the plight of kids like Timothy Hayman and Vincent Tobak, boys perpetually on the low end of the schoolyard totem pole.

The schoolyard bell rang and we all fell into line and marched into our classrooms. For everyone else the incident was just a passing bit of comedy that had come and gone. Unable to concentrate in class, I continued to feel terrible about it. Along with the initial insult, I couldn't help thinking about how mad my mom was going to be if she found out about it. I hid out behind the cafeteria during recess and took my shoe off, trying to push back the dent, but it wouldn't budge. Throughout the day I kept imagining that my shoe stood out to everyone else as if it were a giant clown shoe that you would see on Bozo. I couldn't wait for the school day to end. I was already imagining how I would toss and turn that night over the incident while Richie Carpano slept like a baby.

When I finally got home, I quickly dropped my school books on the table and skulked up to my attic room - a personal sanctuary in good times and bad. I tried several things before I finally succeeded in pushing the dent out with the end of a broom handle. They weren't steel toes after all. I ran downstairs and got my dad's shoeshine kit, opened up the Kiwi Brown, and polished and buffed the toe of my shoe repeatedly. I didn't get it perfect, but I got it good enough that my mom probably wouldn't notice.

Just like so many things when you're a kid, the gravity and insult of the whole thing faded within a few days. I kept myself a good distance from Carpano whenever it was possible. There were certainly worse incidents occurring in the schoolyard - some involving him and some not. I remember sometime later that year seeing him berated harshly by Sister Carolita in front of the whole class for some infraction. He stood there slouching in his St. Mary's uniform, humiliated, a refugee from another school, hair falling into his blushing face, blocking the tears that he was fighting. I actually felt bad for him. Despite what he did, I somehow had an understanding and compassion for what he was feeling, and a sense that the same was lacking in him.

A lot happened at St. Mary's in the following few years. The shortage of people willing to enter a religious vocation made it necessary for the school to hire more lay teachers - educators who were mere civilians, not nuns or priests. With that came an awakening in many of us. Mr. Burns, Mr. Donovan, Miss Walusiak, and a few others were modern, young, fascinating people who began to show us that there were other sides to life than those we had been exposed to so far. They actually seemed to take an interest in our thoughts and ideas. Their presence in the schoolyard helped to settle things down as well.

Times and attitudes were changing quickly. The Catholic church and those associated with it were reluctantly pulled along. Parents began to take notice of their kids being hit or ridiculed. Misters Burns and Donovan brought an awareness of modern literature and music into the classroom. The acoustic guitar made its first appearance at a few of the Masses. We were even granted permission to study the rock opera "Jesus Christ Superstar" in English class - a huge deal at the time.

There were still bullies of course, as there always are. I moved on to St. Raphael's for ninth grade to start a new adventure with the Christian Brothers and a melting pot of other students from all parts of Pawtucket. Richie Carpano and Norman Beladeau went to LaSalle as freshmen. I often wondered how Richie managed, once again the new kid, with older, bigger, smarter people all around him. Suddenly a small fish in a vast ocean.

Bullies come in many shapes and sizes. You work with them. You play with them. Sometimes they dress in black and white, or blue. Sometimes they live in your house. Throughout history many have ruled countries, run businesses, managed sports teams, and owned or manipulated people in countless ways - making someone else small so that they feel bigger.

Occasionally, to your dismay, you may have even seen one in the mirror.

A damaged shoe doesn't seem like an event that should leave a lasting memory, but I suppose it may have been my introduction to the cruel and thoughtless nature that resides in some people. When you're a kid and that door is opened, you never forget it. Lots of years pass and many things happen with the give and take of life, but you can usually spot those of a certain character and the darkness that can be lurking within.

The events at St. Mary's school with Richie Carpano were a long time ago. Yet I still carry that thing with me that he left there. Despite the hurt and the anger at the time, I like to think that I learned from the incident. My sincere hope is that in all these years since, I've never left a dent in anyone else's shoe.

Rick Billings lives in Barrington with his wife Kathy and Nala the wonder dog. "Bully" is a true story. The names of the classmates have been changed to protect the innocent and the guilty. Respectfully dedicated to Gerry Burns - an exemplary teacher who taught that there was an outside the box to think about.

GHOSTS

by Debra Zannelli

SABINE

"Sabine." Ulf's voice, a screechy whine, makes me cringe.

"What?"

Then came the pout. He always pouts when I snap at him, so I bend to look him directly in the eyes. I force my voice to be softer. "What's wrong?" I ask.

"Mom won't answer. I'm sure you know, you know everything."

I wish I did, but there's so much I don't know and worse, there are so many things I know without understanding why. My answer, no matter what I say, won't be good enough for the boy who has an endless stream of questions. "I don't know everything, but I'll answer you if I can."

That ended the pout.

"Do you hear the ghosts?"

"There's no such thing as ghosts," I tell him. His pout tells me that's not what upset him.

"It's bad enough the bakery closed, but now the jewelry store is closed too. I was going to buy an amulet, you know, to protect me from the ghosts." Ulf's bottom lip trembles. "I haven't seen Abel all week. We were supposed to get together. He said he'd give me some babka."

"The Herschhoffs have moved. They went to live with family."

"Where?" Ulf asks.

This was more demand than question. Stalling for time, I bend to tie my tied shoe, and hope he won't notice. His tapping foot tells me he did notice. "In America." I knew it was a mistake as soon as I said it.

"They don't have family in America. I didn't think you'd lie to me, Sabine."

Watching him storm out of the room, I wonder why I feel so bad about the lie. He's eight, he'll get over it. Still, it bothers me and I almost follow him, to explain what I know, but it's for our and the ghost's safety that he doesn't know. It's bad enough a word spoken to the wrong person could change our lives in ways I don't want to imagine. I thought of what my mother said, the warning.

"If anyone asks about Ulf, about his ghosts, you must tell them he has a vivid imagination, that every creak this old house makes sounds like voices to him." She'd spoken with desperation, seeming to age with each word. "Give me a kiss, I have to get to work."

As she walked out the door, with a basket of cleaning tools in hand, I heard her recite her nightly prayers.

Krista

Every time I walk out the door, I worry. I look back, even though I know Sabine will have locked the door behind me. The things I hear in the houses I clean sicken me. I can't afford to let them see how I feel. There's only me now. I need the money. I look at the dark streets. I know it's early, the sun has not yet risen, but once, the bright lights streaming from store windows would have made the morning less dark. It doesn't take long to get to the Levis and I'm glad when I draw near. But something is wrong and I hesitate to enter.

The usual greeting remains unsaid. Teary-eyed, she reaches out and takes my hand. "Krista, we need your help. I thought we had more time, but they're coming tomorrow."

I don't ask who is coming. I already know. "Tonight then."

I push past her and begin the dusting. I hope to finish before my children come home from school.

Sabine

It's been a long time since I've seen my father. He left wearing a freshly cleaned uniform and spit-polished shoes. The morning sun that flowed into the room made the golden cross he wore glow. He walked out the door without a glance at me, even when I called him.

I thought I'd miss him, but the father I knew had left long before he stepped out the door. It started with his meetings. Each night he'd come home angrier than when he'd left. His words were hard. Our neighbors, the ones he used to like, were spoken of with wrath. Last night he hit my mother. They were arguing. Like all the husbands and wives I knew, they argued, but he'd never raised his hand in anger. The bruise on my mother's cheek was vivid, the traces of my father's beefy hand clear. For the first time that I could remember, I felt hatred. It's sad that the first person I hated was my father. The second person I hated was the one everyone was talking about. His words were repeated with reverence. I'd heard their belief that he would bring them the future they craved. The hatred he spoke, his lies were so often repeated, every word spoken as a prayer. It was hard realizing how the people I'd grown up with had changed.

The night the bakery closed, my mother was late coming home. I was worried, but kept my fear away from my brother. When she walked in, her steps were faulty; she almost stumbled as she headed to the kitchen.

"Could you sleep in your brother's room tonight?" Mother always told us what to do in the form of a question.

"Yes." I didn't ask why, but I didn't sleep in his room. Waiting until Mom went downstairs, I slipped out the door and crouched on the stairs where I knew I couldn't be seen. When the darkness of night blanketed the house, our back door opened. I heard shuffling feet, people walking in slippers, not shoes, and I went to see what was going on. They weren't surprised when I walked in. They were terrified.

"It's okay. I'll take you." I turned to my mother. "If Ulf wakes, it would be best if he saw you."

That's when Ulf started talking about ghosts and I learned how to steal.

Our house, the oldest on the street, had been built beside the old root cellar. It was my mother's parents' home and long before I was born the root cellar's opening had been cemented over. My mother, having grown up there, knew about it. I don't know how or even if it was my mother who made the door. Less than three feet high and just a little above two feet wide, it was hard to see. Mother put the laundry cot in front to make it invisible. Only one other person knew it existed. I used to pray that my father would come home - the man who played with his children, the man who made his wife laugh. Now I prayed he'd never return.

It wasn't long before the bakery closed. Four more people slipped into the cellar. Mom didn't ask me to steal, but I knew a family of three wouldn't need enough food for ten. I got caught once, but since I was seen only grabbing an apple, the punishment was just a slap on the hand. It's a good thing they didn't see the meat I'd strapped around my waist. My loose shirt covered the bulge. I did hear a titter or two. Old ladies wondering how a girl my age could get pregnant. That meant I had six more months to hide food under my dress.

Being scared wasn't the worst thing. The buckets made me ill. It fell to me to take the waste away. The pails couldn't be emptied more than once every few days. Ulf thought it was funny when he caught me digging holes in the back yard, but he believed me when I told him I was playing pirate, burying make-believe treasure.

ULF

I don't know when it began, only that I was too young to understand. The day I turned thirteen, I hoped they'd understand it was time to let me help. I never believed in ghosts, but I knew that the voices I heard weren't imaginary. I was curious but not unaware of what was going on. The town changed. Some of my friends were taken from their homes while their neighbors jeered. I saw toys once held in loving hands taken by people with lustful faces. When the butcher was taken from the office, his wife and two children disappeared, and three more ghosts were welcomed into my home. Sabine worked hard. She brought home more food than other families but ate less than anyone I knew. I lost my appetite when I saw her sucking on the bones of the chicken we'd roasted. She always made sure I had enough.

Today is the day. I'm turning fourteen. It's also the day when I have to pass the test and it terrifies me. I still attend school. My lessons consist of learning how to obey. Anything else is second to that one idea, and that's where the test comes in. First there is obeying the command, then there's trusting the others, those who took the test last year. Of course, they're the ones who passed. Those who failed aren't here anymore. I'm pretty sure they aren't anywhere. There are usually a lot of tears following the test.

There's no saying no. So I'm standing on a ledge, twenty feet above the gymnasium floor. Two boys are waiting for me. Their job is to catch me, and mine is to let myself fall. You can't face them for that part of the test. You must use blind trust, that's all part of the obeying. It's only knowing my sister and mother need me to help protect the ghosts that keeps me standing. Only knowing they'll mourn my loss if I don't fall that makes me step back.

The boys caught me, and though I didn't hit the floor, it doesn't mean it didn't hurt. Before I leave, I get a gun. It's expected that we'll know how to shoot before classes begin again. Once I can shoot, I'll go into the army, and I'll defeat the enemies I've been hearing about for as long as I remember. Or I'll die a brave soldier, fighting for the fatherland. I stand, not listening to the applause, and turn to see my mother's pale face. Tears stream from her eyes as she hangs onto my sister. Sabine looks more terrified than Mom. It hurts but I know what she's afraid of.

The banquet celebrating those who passed the test has more food than I've seen in a year. There's enough to feed all the boys and their families, but only a little more than half of us made it. The funerals will be full of pomp and circumstance. Only a couple of their families remain for the feast. Between the cheering and other festivities, I'm often alone. It's surprising how much food I can hide in my uniform. I've grown, but I'm still small for my age. The teacher believed me when I told him I wanted a size larger so I could grow into it. Now, like the ghosts in my house, no one sees me.

"Can we go home?" I ask my mother, but I'm looking at Sabine.

"Of course."

I like when my mother's hand brushes the hair off my forehead.

"You're burning up. Are you sick?" Her question is answered by my sister before I have a chance to reply.

"Of course he's not feeling well. He could have died. Ulf's not a fool."

Sabine looked into my eyes, and I realized that she saw me as an equal. "We should get going. The smell of pastrami is making me sick."

The warning. I reek of food, and even though the teachers are occupied, the smell won't go unnoticed. When we get home, with the door locked behind us, Sabine helps me take off the coat. She catches the meat and rolls before they land on the floor. "You want to come with me, say hi to the ghosts?"

I ignore my crying mother. I know why she's crying and my chest puffs just a little. This is the real test and I'm proud to say I passed. I did what my father, what most of the people in the town, can't do. I have compassion. You don't need to be cold and cruel to be a man.

Abel is so skinny. His ruddy complexion has turned to a pasty white. I thought the food would be grabbed and gobbled by people living only one meal away from starvation, but they share. Parents pass food to their children, who take only what they need. The boys at school steal food from the plates of their friends. Another lesson learned.

A young man fit to enter the school of higher—that's a laugh—education has a little more freedom before he loses it all. The best thing about this is my being able to get more food and that I can get close to the broadcasting station.

I begin speaking as soon as I return. "Mom, Sabine, we're losing the war. The invasions have begun."

When my mother doesn't respond, I turn to Sabine.

"It's good news but it means they'll want you to join the army even sooner," Sabine replies, her tears making the words jumpy.

"I won't fight for them." It hits me then. If I don't fight, they'll kill me. If I do fight, I'll die in places inside me, even if my body survives. "I have to think."

I leave them behind as my mother sobs. I know I can't run. The police will look for me. They'll tear the house apart, find the ones we've been hiding. There is something, but I'm loathe to take the necessary steps. Night creeps down, pressing on me. I'm still walking when the sun begins its slow rise. This is it. I've made my decision. I hope my mother understands. I hope I'll live to explain.

SABINE

I know what Ulf's going to do. I can't stop him. I'm not sure I should. What I do know is I have to be there. It might make the difference between caring for him or burying him. Carefully avoiding the ever-growing piles of horse manure, I walk to the grocery store. I don't know how supplies are brought to the cities, but our supplies come by cart. Big horses pulling heavy loads. They're jumpy, the horses. Some come from battles, wounded. The grocery store isn't far. The carts are pulling up to the loading dock when I see my brother. I hear the gunshot at the same time I see the horse buck. The grocer's wife screams, the horse lunges. Ulf steps between them and pushes her to safety. For a moment I can't breathe. My pounding chest heaves with each running step. Houses empty as people come out to see. Only Jurgen, the undertaker, steps onto the road. People usually shy away from him. His profession holds him apart, but he's a brave man. Even with only one good leg, the reason he's not in the army, he still gets to my brother before me.

Jurgen takes the horse's weight on his broad back and gives me enough time to pull Ulf away. There's blood, and Ulf holds his broken arm across his face. But there's also a smile and a conspiratorial whisper. "Good plan, don't you think?"

"Absolutely."

The cart that usually carries caskets is wheeled over.

"No horses," Jurgen yells. "He's had enough of horses. I'll pull, you get him on top, easy now, easy. Sabine, you're coming with me. Vina, tell Mrs. Winkler. We're going to the doc."

"Ulf, squeeze my hand as hard as you can. Don't let go." It hurts to see how little strength he has, but his grip is real and his hand doesn't fall away.

Ulf moans when they move him. I don't want him to be in pain, but his moan tells me he's still with us. Mom arrives, a fist stuffed into her mouth to keep screams from escaping. It seems like forever but finally the doctor approaches.

"Sabine, Krista." The doctor is serious, but there's a little smile playing with his upper lip. I just can't return it.

"Ulf will be fine. Brave boy stopping the horse the way he did. His leg is shattered. I'll do the best I can, but he'll never walk right. His right arm, he's right-handed?"

Mom nods. I reply, "Yes."

"I saved it, but he'll have to learn to use his left one for finer work. He can learn how to write with it. We all could if we tried hard enough. It'll be a while before he can stand without help. He'll probably try to push himself, but with enough time, he'll heal. I know this is awful news, but he can't join the army. I'll sign the necessary forms.

ULF

I write with my left hand. You'd never know I wasn't born left-handed. The accident did what I hoped and I got to remain home. It was a good thing, too. The war was drawing to a close, and it made desperate people more desperate. There was a push to hide their crimes. Houses were searched. I followed with lurching steps as they conducted an inspection of my home. People invariably felt bad for the hero-cripple and I always got an extra helping. The ghosts got more food. I can't do the stairs so I haven't seen my friends. Today that changes. The allies arrived and our war is over. Under guard of American soldiers, the ghosts are finally going to walk in the sun. The soldiers are my age. Our faces aren't very different. The war they fought has made them rough, but they still smile. They gave Sabine chocolate, and she gave half to me amidst much laughing.

It's almost time, and I find myself nervous. The hand that moves so seldom is twitching. The twitching stops when Abel runs over. He gives me a hug I fear will break my ribs. I look at the boy - now a man - who stands inches above me but weighs half what I weigh, and I see a smile. His skin is so pale. The others, too. The light plays in Sabine's dark blue eyes.

"The ghosts, we set them free."

Debra Zannelli is the author of the Darkness and Light Trilogy. Her short story "The Quiet One" was published in *Dark Winter Literary Magazine*, and her poem, "The Journey," was published in *Rhode Island Bards Poetry Anthology* of 2022. Visit her website drzannelliauthor.com or find her on Facebook: debradarknight.

POETIC JUSTICE

By Kara Marziali

In a dark time, the eye begins to see.

My husband introduced me to Theodore Roethke's poetry during our courtship. At that time, Charlie was a hotshot attorney, advancing quickly at my father's firm. Charlie worked hard during the week and played hard on the weekend. Whether he was in a court of law or on the tennis court, Charlie's only aim was to win. He convinced me that he read poetry to round out his intellect. Charlie explained that Roethke was one of the most accomplished and influential poets of his generation. What Charlie failed to mention was that the poet-intellect was equally known for his nervous breakdowns.

In a dark time, the eye begins to see.

Ironically, my dark time was also marked by mental illness—minus the poetry, pomp, or publicity. It was my own private madness. Pretending, performing, and play-acting. At odds with my circumstances and shadows of my husband's past, I feigned my wellbeing with an overexaggerated smile, garden parties, and designer handbags. I hid explosive sobs and hard edges for the sake of my husband's public persona.

In the interest of Charlie's political career, I accompanied him on campaign trails and fundraising events. I stoked his ego, promoted his self-aggrandizing rhetoric, and mimicked his partisan bullshit. I allowed him to speak for me, limiting my responses to phrases such as, "Really?" and "I see." Charlie's authority over me knew no limits. I accepted his insolence and made excuses for his boorish behavior to the children, my parents, and the Junior League. Ever the dutiful wife, my compromises continued in the bedroom.

In a dark time, the eye begins to see.

On one such occasion, I fixed him a cocktail before heading upstairs for the night. I often retreated early and feigned sleep, hoping he would not insist on waking me to have sex. I knew he was satisfying his lustful desires with a Senate page, some high school junior who apparently delivered more than correspondence and legislative materials. She called him at home that night. He was on the phone in the den sipping Jack Daniels while I listened silently, using the phone on the bedside table. I expected to hear a sexually overt exchange intended to provoke my husband's arousal. Instead, I learned of something more salacious.

In a dark time, the eye begins to see.

Charlie's naturally imposing voice was measured and punctuated with a sense of urgency. Persuasive, serious, insistent. A brief conversation peppered with imperatives. Now. Necessary. Quietly. Quickly. I hung up the phone before I was detected and before I knew the full extent of his actions.

In a dark time, the eye begins to see.

Without delay I crawled under the covers and switched off the light. As I lay there simulating sleep, I heard his footsteps on the stairs. His cadence matched my racing heartbeat. The rhythmic thumping sound drummed in my ears. When he reached the top of the stairs, I heard the cock of his pistol. As he brazenly approached the bedside, I could smell the whiskey on his breath.

In a dark time, the eye begins to see.

In the dark, I saw the hulking figure of my husband stagger. The pistol fell from his hand as he clutched his chest. Confused. Confounded. Soon enough the sound of his labored breathing blended with the vomit caught at the back of his throat. Gurgle. Grunt. Grope. My laughter drowned out his pitiful gasps. I knew the arsenic had finally killed him. Fallen. Fatal. Finished.

In a dark time, the eye begins to see.

Kara Marziali is the author of *Kara Koala and Her Kaleidoscope of Feelings*. When Kara is not with family and friends, you can find her crafting, painting, journaling, singing, or dancing. Although she has survived her own personal "dark times," she identifies as a "cockeyed optimist."

FROM DARKNESS INTO LIGHT: EDDIE'S STORY

by Barbara Ann Whitman

One. Two. Three. Four. Eddie's fingertips tapped the edge of the Formica counter. Only the index and middle fingers. Always the right hand. It was the only way.

Entering the small kitchen, he punched the power button on the coffeemaker and waited a few seconds until he heard the reassuring gurgle as it came to life. *One. Two. Three. Four.* This time, on the refrigerator door. He opened it, feeling the rush of cool air across his forearm as he reached for the milk carton, sitting square in the center of the door's interior. A cursory glance, as the door closed, confirmed that none of the items on the scarce shelves were touching one another. That would be bad. Very bad.

Eddie reached for the cabinet, his fingers brushing the dull brass handle before he retracted it violently. *Close call. Stupid. Stupid. Stupid.* He silently admonished himself. *One. Two. Three. Four.* On the front of the cabinet, perfectly centered. Opening the cabinet, he let out his breath and grabbed a mug. Again, he found comfort in the simplistic order of things. Plates on the top shelf. Bowls on the middle shelf. Mugs on the bottom. All safely occupying their own space.

He took his coffee to the chair and sat. Before taking a sip of the steamy goodness, he looked around his modest, two-room apartment. The shades were perfectly straight and covered exactly half of the window.

On the small couch, two throw pillows were at identical angles, each at opposite ends of the cushions. The vintage ceramic cookie jar sat dead center on the round kitchen table. Two chairs tucked in all the way, facing each other across the shiny, but worn, maple surface.

With his shoulders slouched in relief, Eddie sipped his coffee and swallowed. *Should I recheck the bedroom?* He knew with certainty that he had inspected it thoroughly before coming into the kitchen. But the close call with the cabinet door had unnerved him. Recalling what his social worker had taught him, he did a 'mental inventory.' He closed his eyes and pictured the bedroom as he left it. Bed made, rug straightened, shades up halfway, closet door shut tightly. The image soothed him.

The only unknown was Elvis, his twelve-pound tabby. Eddie pictured him curled up against his pillow in the center of the bed. The cat never slept with him, but waited patiently while Eddie made the bed every morning before jumping up and settling in for his morning nap, right where Eddie laid his head every night.

Although caffeine is a stimulant, it calmed his nerves. It was warm and welcoming because it always tasted the same. He always used the same mug, the one with 'Edward' etched onto the front. That was his childhood name. He was Eddie now. He sat in his chair and sipped. Then he was ready to face the day, cautiously. He knew when he left the building there were people who didn't understand him and would stare, whisper, or even laugh. Even though it hurt his feelings, there was nothing he could do. He had to tap and count. If he became careless, the voices might come back.

When he was twelve, Edward was sitting in the school library and thought people were whispering behind the stacks. But there was no one there. Then he heard it again, a few days later, while he was doing homework in his bedroom, alone. Edward had looked in the closet and under the bed. No one there. This went on for nearly a year. He couldn't make out what they were saying except for his name every once in a while. He was afraid to tell anyone, so he tried to ignore them. Usually, it worked. Until it didn't.

If he was at home, he'd cover his ears. Then he figured out that his ear buds helped, so he just cranked the music. The rhythm helped. *One. Two. Three. Four.* The voices couldn't compete with the music and the beat. *One. Two. Three. Four.* His mother wasn't happy when he didn't respond to her calling to him from downstairs or even right outside his door. She sighed and decided it was just a phase.

Sometimes he'd lay in bed at night and listen when the voices were too loud to ignore. Edward started thinking of the loudest voice as Abner, after his grandfather's favorite comic strip, "Li'l Abner." When Edward was very small, his grandpa would read him comics. The humor was beyond a child, but he liked the way it made his grandfather laugh. It was sort of like that - he could hear the voices but didn't always understand.

He began avoiding classmates at school and neighborhood pick-up baseball games. He was afraid they'd somehow find out about the voices. The more time he spent alone, the more the voices talked. The louder they became. Sometimes they'd try to tell Edward to say bad things. He resisted. Then they started to tell him to *do* bad things. It scared him because he began believing he would have to do the bad things to keep the voices happy. But Abner came to his rescue and told the others to shut up. Edward eventually thought of Abner as a friend.

*

Mrs. Roberts was writing on the chalkboard with her back to the class when she heard shrieks and moving furniture. She spun around, expecting a prank, and prepared her angry face. Instead, she dropped the chalk and nearly screamed herself. Edward was seated at his desk, staring at his hand, which was palm-down on his desk top, gushing blood. There was a newly sharpened Number 2 pencil standing straight up in the middle of the wound. The other eighth graders had moved away from him; they dragged their desks and made sounds of repulsion. This left Edward sitting in the center of the room, with blood pooling on his desk, like a scene from a horror film.

"Someone run to the office and get the nurse!" the teacher managed to shout. "And the principal." Some of the students were nearly in hysterics. Except for Edward. He simply stared at his hand as though it belonged to someone else. Mrs. Roberts ushered the other students out of the classroom and into the hallway.

Other teachers arrived, having heard the commotion. "Watch them," she yelled, and went back into the classroom. Edward hadn't moved. She grabbed as many paper towels as she could from above the little sink against the wall and approached him. She didn't know what to do and feared she could make the injury worse. "Edward," she said in a soothing voice. "Help is on the way. Tell me who did this to you." He didn't respond. He looked very pale. *What's taking them so long?* she wondered.

The nurse burst into the room and saw the blood. "Has anyone called an ambulance?" Mrs. Roberts shook her head. The principal sauntered in, obviously having underestimated the situation. "Holy...." he began.

"Call a rescue, now!" the nurse shouted at him. He turned and headed for the door, apparently glad for a reason to escape. Mrs. Roberts placed a hand gently on Edward's shoulder and stooped until she was at eye level with him. "You have to tell me who did this to you," she said in a firm but kind voice. He looked from her to the nurse and back again. "Abner," was all he said before he passed out.

Eddie took his empty cup to the sink. *One. Two. Three. Four.* He turned on the faucet and rinsed out his cup. He picked up the carton of milk. *One. Two. Three. Four.* He opened the refrigerator and placed it back in the middle. Elvis strutted into the kitchen, stopping to stretch and yawn. "Too late," Eddie said. "Milk's already back in the fridge." The cat slalomed between his ankles until Eddie bent and scooped him up. Elvis purred as Eddie snuggled him against his face, whispering in his ear, "Good kitty. Who's daddy's good boy?"

Getting a pet had been his social worker's idea. 'Pet therapy,' she had called it. "Someone to keep you company." Eddie hadn't warmed to the idea so she eventually dropped it. But later he considered it; he thought

225

about the pros and cons for a long time. He thought about what it would be like. He looked around for the animal, expecting one to materialize, momentarily forgetting that he had only imagined it.

Eddie went to the local animal shelter. He was afraid they'd know that he was different and deny him a pet. Eddie walked out into the kennel to look at the dogs. They all started barking at once. The dogs ran to the ends of their individual cages and jumped at the gates, shaking and rattling the chain link. It was so loud that he had to cover his ears and run back out into the lobby. He couldn't breathe and frantically looked for something to count. Cinderblock walls. *One. Two. Three. Four. One. Two. Three. Four. One. Two. Three. Four.* Eddie's focus returned and he was able to remove his hands from his ears. Luckily, nobody witnessed the spectacle.

"Do you have anything quieter?" he asked the woman behind the desk. She didn't laugh at him. Instead, she said, "How about a cat?" and directed him toward the cat room. The cages were built into the wall. There were three double rows and each held one cat. Most were sleeping or ignored Eddie. But the biggest was a butterscotch-colored tabby that rubbed himself against the metal rungs of his cage, purring so loudly that he reminded Eddie of a motorboat. He took the index card out of the slot above the cage and brought it to the desk. He paid $75 but the kind woman said it was really a donation. And she gave Eddie a sturdy cardboard carrier and a bag of cat food. "What are you going to call him?" the shelter woman asked. Eddie shrugged as he watched her stuff the cat into the carrier. The tabby was not pleased and struggled as she closed the top.

One. Two. Three. Four. Eddie opened the car door and lifted the carrier onto the front passenger seat. He tossed the bag of food onto the floor. *One. Two. Three. Four.* He got in and started the car. "You ain't nothin' but a hound dog" blared from the radio speakers. The irony of hearing the song at an animal shelter made Eddie chuckle. The tabby meowed with gusto, expressing his feelings about being confined to the carrier. "You ain't nothin' but a hound dog, cryin' all the time."

"Elvis," Eddie said with satisfaction. "I'm going to call you Elvis."

"Abner?" the school nurse asked, looking at the teacher.

Mrs. Roberts shook her head. "I don't know any Abner. Not in my class. Not in any class."

"A nickname?" the nurse suggested. The teacher continued to shake her head.

The ambulance arrived with sirens blaring and the EMTs tended to Edward, who was not fully conscious but moaned softly and made some undecipherable sounds. The nurse rode to the hospital with him and told the emergency room staff what she knew, including the part about Abner. They assured her that Edward's mother was on her way. So, the nurse returned to school to fill out the required paperwork.

A surgeon stitched up Edward's hand and wrapped it in bandages. He explained how to keep it dry and clean. "Do either of you have any questions?" he asked. Neither Edward nor his mother spoke. The doctor instructed his mother how to administer the prescribed pain meds, once the numbing agent wore off, and reminded them of a follow up appointment. His mother took the written prescription and said only, "Thank you." Edward thought he was in the clear. But a new doctor knocked gently on the door before entering. He introduced himself as the psychiatrist on call and asked for a few moments of their time.

Edward fell back against the pillows and closed his eyes. His mind raced, scrambling for a story that would explain his injury. *Anything but the truth,* he thought. But there was no time. He kept his eyes closed while the new doctor spoke to his mother. "Has anything like this happened before?"

His mother murmured no. She had no explanation. No, Edward's behavior had not changed recently. No, he had not complained of headaches. No, there had been no noticeable changes to his sleeping or appetite or grades.

"If you don't mind stepping out for a few minutes, I'd like to talk with Edward alone."

Edward opened his eyes just enough to confirm that his mother was, in fact, leaving him alone with the psychiatrist. The doctor looked at Edward for a long moment and just smiled. "Can I get you something, Edward - maybe a cold drink?"

"I just want to go home."

"We can talk about that. But first, we need to try to understand what happened to you today and how your hand was injured. Can you tell me a little bit about that?"

"I don't remember. All I know is I woke up in the rescue squad and the school nurse was there and my hand was bleeding."

"What's the last thing you remember about being in class today?"

Edward closed his eyes again, buying time. He wasn't an experienced liar, but he just couldn't tell the doctor the truth. The scene replayed in his mind. The voices had been loud all morning. He had wished he was at home where he could use his ear buds. He tried to hear the music in his head, hoping it would drown out the voices. He realized he was rocking back and forth in his seat, mentally counting the beat. *One. Two. Three. Four.* He felt the stares of his classmates, who were looking at him funny. So he stopped.

"Take your time, Edward. Try to remember," the psychiatrist said.

He couldn't hear the music when he stopped rocking. That's when Abner started shouting at him, calling Edward names. He was scared because Abner wasn't ever mean before. "You're so stupid!" he shouted. "Stupid. Stupid. Stupid. Everybody's looking at you. They know about me." Edward tried to make the music play in his head again. He started rocking, and counted silently. His eyes were shut tightly against the noise. Abner was yelling, "I won't go away. They will all hear me. You can't stop me unless you do what I say." *One. Two. Three. Four. One. Two. Three. Four.* "Stab your hand with your pencil. Do it now. Do it or I'll cut your hand off myself! Do. It. Now."

Elvis ran straight under the bed upon release from the carrier. That's where he stayed for the rest of the day. Before bedtime, Eddie got down on his hands and knees with a flashlight to confirm that the cat was alright. Elvis backed into the farthest corner so all Eddie could see were two green eyes shining back at him. *What if he never comes out? How will he eat?* He considered pushing a bowl of cat food under the bed or maybe a saucer of milk. Eddie slept fitfully, wondering if he had made a mistake.

In the morning, Elvis strolled into the kitchen as Eddie was making coffee. He sniffed the air twice, ignoring his new master, and headed to the bathroom, where he promptly relieved himself in the litter box. That was that. It was as if the cat had always lived there.

Eddie had been in the habit of putting out his medications the night before, carefully counting, rechecking the bottles, and placing the pills in a small ramekin beside the coffee maker. One morning, he discovered the ramekin on its side and his pills scattered everywhere. He desperately gathered them, one by one. They were on the counter, on the floor, under the table. Elvis was nowhere to be found. Eddie placed the pills in a straight line, from largest to smallest. This was difficult, given that his hands were shaking. Then he counted them. He counted them again. He thought they were all there, but he needed to be certain. *One. Two. Three. Four.* He opened the cabinet where he kept the prescription bottles and took them out, placing each one beside the corresponding pill. None were missing. Eddie counted them all again to calm his nerves. When his hands stopped shaking, he got a drink of water and swallowed them.

He found Elvis sound asleep in his usual spot on the bed, oblivious to the commotion he had caused. Eddie stroked the cat's head and scratched behind his ears, as relief flooded through his body. *What did I forget?* It had been some time since the bad things happened. Eddie checked the room. Closet door closed. Blinds halfway. Rug straight. He headed for the other room. *One. Two. Three. Four.* Window blinds. Cookie jar. Chairs. Throw pillows. *The pills. I shouldn't have left them on the counter. Stupid, stupid, stupid.*

That afternoon, Eddie went to the pharmacy and purchased a weekly med dispenser with a little plastic compartment for each day, Monday through Sunday. He remembered his mother used one for her pills, when she was living at the nursing home. When he got home, he closed

Elvis in the bedroom while he counted out a week's medication, lining each pill up in front of each daily section before placing them inside and pressing down to close all seven lids. *One. Two. Three. Four.* Monday. *One. Two. Three. Four.* Tuesday. *One. Two. Three. Four.* Wednesday. It took him an hour.

That night, he tried to watch a television show, but he couldn't concentrate. He was still reliving the incident with the scattered pills. *Stupid. Stupid. Stupid.* Throughout the day, he had checked on Elvis repeatedly. Even though he knew there were no pills missing, Eddie couldn't get over the feeling that his carelessness could have killed his only friend.

Before the psychiatrist would allow Edward's mother to take him home, he had to sign a paper promising he wouldn't hurt himself. Edward and his mother had to agree to certain things, such as safety check-ins every 30 minutes for 24 hours and calling the Crisis Hotline if he felt "unsafe." The whole thing seemed ridiculous to Edward. *How can I be safe from somebody no one can see? How can you keep me safe from my own hands?* But they were both tired and hungry and wanted nothing more than to go home. They also agreed to weekly therapy appointments at the hospital's mental health clinic and an intake appointment was scheduled for the following day.

Edward's mother drove home in silence for the first few miles. He knew that closing his eyes was not going to work this time. Finally, she spoke. "Maybe you can explain to me why you'd protect whoever did this? You were *stabbed*, Edward! If Abner is a nickname for someone, you need to cut the crap and tell me who he is."

So, she does know. Edward didn't know if the school or the hospital had told her everything. "I don't want to talk about it, Mom."

"Well, you're going to have to talk about it. And talk about it. And talk about it some more. What do you think this therapy is going to be about? They think you're hearing things, Edward. Do you have any idea how embarrassing that is? You're thirteen, for God's sake - too old for imaginary friends, don't you think? You need to tell me who did this right now. Then we can let the authorities handle it and we can skip the rest of this nonsense."

Edward looked out the window, avoiding his mother's glare. There was no use telling her the truth - she'd never believe him. He couldn't blame someone else—his entire class had seen what happened. He groaned at the realization that everyone at school would be talking about him. He could never return and face them. Most of all, he had no idea how Abner was going to react. Edward had a feeling that the worst was yet to come.

Eddie stared at the phone. After four rings, he picked up the receiver. "Hello?"

"Is this Edward Callahan?"

"Yes..."

"This is Mercy Hospital calling. Your mother has been admitted to the emergency room here after a fall at the nursing home. You're listed as her next of kin. She hit her head hard but she's conscious. You might want to come as soon as possible."

Eddie tried to process the information. It sounded bad. Very bad.

"Mr. Callahan?"

"Yes, I'm here."

"I tried to reach the other emergency contact. Martin Callahan? The number is disconnected."

"My father," Eddie managed. "I don't know where he is. I haven't seen my mother either... ever since..."

"Do you have another number for Martin? Your mother is asking for him and, well, time is of the essence."

Eddie hung up the phone. He tried to picture his mother in a hospital bed, her head bandaged. But it was the mother he remembered from childhood. *She must look different now.* His version of his mother was the one who refused to take him home from the hospital after the third time. After the voices told him to kill himself and he had nearly succeeded. The mother who told the doctors he was "trying to get attention" and he was "just like his father." The mother who eventually had stopped visiting him at the group home because she found it "too depressing."

He stared at the phone, as if the memories were still streaming from the brief connection with the doctor. He looked away and broke the spell. Shaking off the flashbacks, he sat in his chair. Elvis jumped into his lap and settled there, a rare occurrence. Eddie stroked the cat and concentrated on his breathing. He counted. Inhale. *One. Two. Three. Four.* Hold. *One. Two. Three. Four.* Exhale. *One. Two. Three. Four.*

My father. His was an image Eddie could not conjure from memory. It had simply been too long. He only remembered loud fighting between his parents as he lay in bed at night with his pillow over his head. Years later, when Eddie found the courage to ask, his mother would not answer his questions, only saying that his father "had problems." Eddie eventually stopped asking. His doctor suggested that Eddie may have inherited mental illness from his father. When it manifested, his mother was triggered and, therefore, did not accept Eddie's condition. The doctor even suggested that Eddie try to contact his father, to get a better idea of family history, which might help his treatment. But Eddie figured his father wasn't interested or he would have stayed in touch.

He arrived at the hospital, nervously fingering the anti-anxiety pill in his front pocket. He wasn't supposed to drive if he took an extra dose, but he felt better knowing it was there if he needed it. A nice nurse led him to a small room. Eddie winced as he walked through the door behind her, without tapping. How much worse could things get?

Eddie sat in a hard chair beside the bed and watched his mother's face. Her hair was completely white now and she was so thin. Her eyes were shut, and a wire ran from her index finger to a monitor that beeped rhythmically. *One. Two. Three. Four.* It comforted him. He touched the pill in his pocket. *One. Two. Three. Four.*

An hour passed. Then his mother opened her eyes and looked straight at him. "Martin."

"Mother. It's Eddie. Edward."

"You stay away from that boy. I took good care of him, did it all myself. He still turned out crazy, like you. You've done enough damage. Leave him alone!"

The monitor started beeping faster and an alarm went off. The nurse rushed into the room. She was no longer nice. "Mrs. Callahan? I'm going to give you something to help you calm down."

She turned to Eddie. "I'll need you to step out."

Eddie walked out of the room and kept on walking until he reached the parking lot. He drove home in silence. His mind was numb. His body felt paralyzed. He forgot about the pill in his pocket. He didn't even tap before opening the door to his apartment. Climbing into bed fully clothed, he pulled the covers up to his chin and stared at the ceiling. Elvis jumped onto the bed and sat beside him. Eddie sobbed.

When he awoke, it was dark outside and the phone was ringing. "Hello?"

"Mr. Callahan? It's the hospital calling. You should come right away."

"I'm not coming back. I can't come back."

"Mr. Callahan. I'm very sorry to tell you that your mother has passed away. It was peaceful and her nurse was with her. I'm sorry that there was no time to call you before it happened."

Eddie spent the rest of the night in his chair, with Elvis on his lap sleeping quietly. He couldn't go back to bed. That's where he was when the bad thing happened. When his mother died. Now he was alone.

When it was light outside, Eddie got up and made his coffee. He knew he should be doing something, but he had no idea what. He couldn't think. He couldn't feel. *Maybe I should skip my pills today.* His mother used to say the meds made him dull. *Maybe she was right.*

Eddie made the bed and checked the room. Blinds halfway. Closet door closed. Rug straight. He wished he could undo the very bad thing by making everything right.

Edward didn't recall the exact moment when Abner ceased speaking to him. It was a blur of foster homes, group homes, and hospital stays until they finally discovered the right combination of medications that allowed him to function without hearing voices. For a while, he still heard Abner at night. But he was never sure if he was really hearing him or if he had only dreamed of him. The doctors and therapists tried to convince Edward that the tapping and counting did not keep the voices away - it was the medicine working. But he wasn't swayed. He wasn't taking any chances.

He lived in a program with other young men for a year. He went to a special school and finished by getting his GED, because he'd missed so many days while he was in the hospital. The other residents had their own issues, which made it easy for Edward to keep to himself. He liked his things a certain way and would get angry when someone touched them or moved them. So they left him alone.

His mother stopped visiting just before Edward turned 18. She made one last-ditch effort to get him to admit that he had made up everything, including the voices that told him to do the bad things. She still harped on the first incident, even though five years had passed.

"You mean to tell me that you stabbed yourself in the hand with a pencil, in the middle of class, with everyone watching?"

"Nobody else did it, okay? It was me. I did it, Mother. Just like I tried to hurt myself all the other times. The voices told me what to do."

"You're going to be an adult soon, Edward. Don't you want to live a normal life?"

That was the last time he saw her.

Eddie returned to his chair. Elvis had taken up his usual spot on the bed, apparently feeling he was no longer needed. Eddie waited for the numbness to wear off so he'd know what he was supposed to do. The phone rang. He waited for four rings.

"Hello?"

"Mr. Callahan? This is the mortuary at Mercy Hospital. We're calling to see what the arrangements will be for your mother."

He hung up, dropping the phone into its cradle as if it had burned his hand.

The phone rang throughout the day, but he didn't answer. *It's probably the hospital. I don't know what I'm supposed to say.* He sat in his chair and waited. But the answers didn't come. He wished he had a brother or a sister. *I am all alone now. I will be alone forever.* He wished he could go back to the house where he grew up. He wished he had something from that time, like one of his favorite t-shirts, his old baseball glove, or one of his mother's knick-knacks.

Shadows grew long on the wall of his living room. He forgot to eat. It grew dark outside again. He waited for the voices to return and tell him what to do.

He dozed. Someone was calling his name. It sounded far away. "Edward!" Someone was knocking on his door. He stumbled through the small kitchen. Leaving the security chain on, Eddie opened the door a few inches. A well-dressed man stared back. "I am your father, Edward. I've come to help."

Barbara Ann Whitman is the author of the YA novel *Have Mercy*, about a young woman's journey from the foster care system to adulthood. Her writings have appeared in all eight of ARIA's annual anthologies. She enjoys mentoring young writers and facilitates a writers' group at her local library.

HEAL, MY DARLINGS

by Douglas S. Levine

Night falls. Day rises. The two-step dance of our lives, the rhythm of our existences.

My friend Marco and I had shining days, times brightened by shared aspects of our lives. Our families were middle-class with immigrant heritage. His parents were first-generation American and mine were second. We each had a younger sister. Our parents taught us values. Principles. The difference between right and wrong. Honesty, trustworthiness, love, humor. The Golden Rule. The importance of family, respect for others, hard work, time for play, faith, hope.

Marco and I prioritized our classes, especially Classics. We were editors of our high school newspaper, *The Messenger*, named for Mercury, the Roman god. During middle and high school years we contended in mythic battles on tennis courts. Ares swaggered to the baseline and lobbed a spear at his opponent. Mars back-pedaled, wielded his scepter behind the service line, leaped, roared, and delivered an overhead smash. When Marco spiked a tennis ball past me, a frequent event, his eyes were as bright as his smile, his signals—war god to war god—we were still friends.

We shared dark times, too: the Cold War, the specter of nuclear annihilation, duck-and-cover drills. Assassinations of JFK, MLK, and RFK. The riots. The war in Vietnam. The draft lottery assigned random sequence numbers from one to three hundred sixty-five, linked to month and day of one's birth, which dictated the order men were inducted into military service. My number was seven; I recited it, "Double O Seven," and was at one with my hero, James Bond. My other number was 4F, unfit for military service, because of my abysmal eyesight and Coke-bottle eyeglasses. Marco's draft number was three hundred fifty-nine, a virtual assurance like my 4F: We would not face the specter of annihilation in a war many had misgivings about. We could proceed with our plans for college.

Another dark time was the day of our high school senior prom. Marco drove to my home that afternoon to wash, wax, and vacuum our chariots while our partners got spiffed up at the beauty salon. We finished Marco's car before my mother called me to the telephone. My prom date, a junior, had catapulted down the stairs at the high school earlier that day. Her mother explained she broke no bones, sustained no head injury, but was badly bruised, too uncomfortable to walk, and committed to bed rest by the doctor. She would recover but could not go to the prom.

Marco was distraught. "Well. She gets another shot next year." He grumbled, "She was supposed to be at the hairdresser's. What was she doing at school? And what are you supposed to do now? We only get one senior prom in life, my friend." Marco hurled a wet sponge into a bucket and splashed soapsuds on the side of his car. He was inconsolable.

I felt badly for my date but ambivalent about the situation. She was the only girl I thought I could invite to the prom. We had gone to the movies once. Kissed once. I would buy flowers and a get well card to bring to her that afternoon.

"Can't you ask someone else? Anyone?"

I squinted at my fellow war god. I had never seen Marco this desperate. Could I storm the prom myself? No. Not cool. "Man, are you serious? Who'd go last minute? The prom's tonight."

"That's right. And time's a-wasting!" Marco pounded around my jalopy. "There must be somebody. Think! Think for God's sake." Marco raked his hair with his hands.

He was right. There was someone else, another junior in our youth group I had asked out, but she refused. Kindly. She preferred we be friends, and we were. "There's a girl—"

"Call her! Now!"

My invitation to her yielded an unhesitating response. Marco had finished rehabilitating my car when I told him I had a new prom date. "Yahoo!" he yelled as he dumped the wash bucket over his head in triumph. After he cleaned up, we and our classmates had a glorious time and relished this part of our journey toward high school graduation. But Marco was wrong on one point. The next year, my junior-turned-senior friend invited me to her prom, which was my second because of Marco's prodding.

Marco and I attended different colleges. During holidays and semester breaks we rooted for our high school football team on Thanksgiving Day, lost small sums at the dog track, and rekindled our rivalry on the tennis court. We wrapped up our get-togethers with food and nectar of the gods—burgers and beer—at the local Ground Round. There, we celebrated the heroics of the Celtics and Bruins and winced at the flops of the Red Sox.

As we sat with our brews, Marco talked about Pamela, the love of his life. He asked me to be his best man and I sought his thoughts about a bachelor's party. We decided on guests and entertainment: a night out with the boys—Marco's friends, his pop, Pamela's father, and my old man—an early evening at the track with Marco's bets subsidized by the attendees, and a quiet dinner. Pamela would approve. Marco returned the favor as my best man and planned a tranquil party before I married Bev. Marco and I were not two feral and lunatic fellows. We honored our reputations as war gods.

Bev and I moved west and fell out of touch with Marco and Pam. The four of us were consumed by our lives and jobs: Marco in criminology and then health administration, Pamela in social work, Bev in nursing, and me in medical research. After Bev and I returned east we reconnected at Marco and Pam's fortieth wedding anniversary party, a serene-as-a-bachelor's party festivity with family and friends. Marco thanked us for coming and introduced us to his kids, Dean and Johanna, and three beautiful grandchildren. Johanna had followed her dad into health administration as did Dean into law enforcement. Pam was by Marco's side. Her eyes, striking and thoughtful, reflected the celebrants and absorbed the joy in the room. We chuckled at Pam's quirky, bird-like whistle—*cheer, cheer, cheer*—an apt appraisal of the event.

After the anniversary party, four months before the first footfalls of calamity's approach, Marco, Pam, Bev, and I dined at a local trattoria. We chatted about life's downs and ups: Marco's scheduled ankle replacement, perpetual house repairs, Dean's divorce, Johanna's boyfriend's move into her house, Marco and Pam's nest egg for world travel during their retirement, grandchildren, Marco and Pam's upcoming cruise. We tipped our glasses to celebrate life and accept the provisions of the Serenity Prayer.

Marco and I spoke often, shared updates. Two months after Pam's and his cruise, Marco said, "Something's not right." With Pam. With the love of his life.

"What do you mean?"

"Not sure..."

Disasters happen without premonitions: getting T-boned in an intersection by a car that runs a red light, being shot in the street by a stray bullet. Earthquakes shake without warning and lightning strikes out of the blue. Likewise, dementia issues no clear, advance notice. The differences between a mental decline and acute catastrophes are the tempos of impending tragedy and the uncertainty, a cruelty added to the slow recognition of a coming crisis. We were in our sixties. When do signs of age—the pause to remember a name or find a word, misplaced keys, the error in the checkbook—become harbingers of a health problem?

"...We're eating lunch in our kitchen nook and she gets up to go to the bathroom. But she goes the wrong way and stands in our dining room."

"And then?" I asked.

"It was weird. After a minute, I went to her. She looked at me. Those eyes, those beautiful eyes. She didn't recognize me. It was only a few seconds and she came back from wherever she was, giggled, and whistled. And off she went..."

I was concerned but did not want to alarm Marco.

"...so, I decided to call her doctor. We have an appointment tomorrow."

Pam's and Marco's unplanned, local journeys began. Thank God they were not naïve to the workings of the health system. Pam served clients with challenging psychosocial and medical needs during her career. Marco was an expert in how health care was managed.

Pam's evaluation by her doctor yielded suspicions. Her referral to a neurologist confirmed the need to investigate further. Visits were scheduled to monitor. Blood tests were done. Brain scans. The results were disturbing but not definitive. Pam needed a spinal tap.

"Damn it! They had to stick her four times." Marco's tolerance for his own pain was remarkable: I knew from his ankle surgery the month before. But he sounded like he was being drawn and quartered when he described Pam's experience.

"Marco, I'm sorry it wasn't easy. They need spinal fluid to figure out what's going on."

"I know. It's just unfair." Marco choked up. "She was in so much pain...so much. I helped hold her still so they could finish. Pam is the kindest, gentlest person I know. She doesn't deserve this. Any of this. Why is this happening to her?"

Marco did not expect a response. We feared the worst. He and I shared the pangs of our parents' unmerciful deaths from metastatic lung and colon cancer. Professionally, we witnessed our patients' suffering with these and other horrendous maladies. We knew diseases were impassive, pathological processes with no sympathy for their victims and families. A specific diagnosis for Pam could inform possible treatments. Prayer could help, too. Marco was Catholic but dismayed about the Church scandals. I hoped his beliefs, his lifelong faith, would enable his prayers for Pam.

After the spinal tap, the neurologist delivered an opinion: a degenerative disorder of the central nervous system. It was named after the doctors who first described it in the 1920s. Who would want this terrible ailment named after them? It had no cure. It was inevitably progressive and fatal. It claimed its victims within a year. Definitive diagnosis required a brain biopsy or was confirmed at autopsy. Blood tests could be done on family members to determine if they were at risk for a genetic form of the disease. How could Marco deal with Pam's disastrous situation and contemplate the fates of their children at the same time?

"Why Pam?" Marco was in war-god mode to search for specialists, answers, therapies. But for a moment Marco was not Mars: disbelief darkened his eyes. He never would have bet on this. "What are the chances? This happens to one in a million. Why Pam?"

Marco and I hunted the internet. Diet, vitamins, and drugs might slow the disease. Marco found experts. Pam tried everything her doctors recommended. Monitoring continued. One bright light was that Dean and Johanna tested negative for the disorder. The disease was Pam's to bear: She bore it with grace but was not alone.

Marco invited Bev and me to join the family at home. He knew we wanted to see Pam and time was short. Her conversation was limited. She enjoyed our company and registered her understanding with a frequent "Yup" and her occasional whistle. Her eyes glowed with love as she sat with Dean and Johanna and embraced her youngest grandchild on her lap. Marco tried to hide the pain from his hip arthritis. He was past due for surgeries postponed because of Pam's condition.

Bev's and my last memories of Pam were her knowing eyes, her dignity as she stood on the threshold, a tender wave with her hand, and the "Later!" she managed. After, Marco and I talked for months, but he avoided details about Pam's descent. He knew that I knew the prognosis and anguish ahead: memory loss, personality changes, insomnia, incoordination, muscle jerks, trouble swallowing, loss of bodily functions. Marco informed me when they reached the expected milestones: hiring of home health aides to assist in Pam's care, recruitment of hospice services, and admission to the hospice inpatient facility where Marco stayed with Pam and bore witness to her withering during her last three weeks. With Marco, Dean, and Johanna at her bedside, Pam passed away, at peace eight months after her symptoms began.

Among memorial ceremonies I attended, a military service stood out. It was for a colleague's son killed in the Afghanistan war. The official protocol, dozens of women and men in Army dress blues, packed auditorium, procession with the casket, folding and presentation of the flag to the mother of the fallen soldier, playing of "Taps"—orchestrated for one too young and who died in service to our country—signified the honor and reverence we often neglect to offer to precious beings who are alive and with whom we share our priceless lives.

The church service for Pam extended my understanding of tributes that balance loss and celebration of a longer and distinctive life. The losses of Pam's love as wife, mother, grandmother, sister, niece, sister-in-law, and aunt were displayed by Marco's, Dean's, and Johanna's open weeping. The hundreds that gathered cried and commemorated Pam's decades-old virtues, kindnesses, and choices to prioritize admiration, respect, and assistance for family, friends, clients, and work colleagues. Pam's accomplishments in social work were recognized by the commonwealth and drove scores of hospital coworkers to attend alongside Marco's associates. Pam's nature and character were well-known by family and friends and transmitted through her children's accomplishments: Johanna's colleagues filled the pews and Dean's comrades comprised a sea of State Police uniforms. In a speech of remembrance, Pam and Marco's niece described Pam as "one in a million"—not to report Pam was a victim of a rare disease but a remark made in high esteem for what Pam held precious, a life practice of generosity that can be so rare.

The pain from Pam's passing was evident among the congregants. Marco's pain was three-fold greater. He had waited too long for treatment and was disabled by agonizing stabs in both of his hips as he mourned for the love of his life. He could not negotiate the distance between the parking lot and interior of the church with a cane or walker. Dean pushed Marco in a wheelchair in and out of the church and aided his father in and out of the pew and out of and back into the limousine that transported the family to the cemetery. Marco had ignored the torment inflicted by his arthritis in his effort to scale a Mount Olympus. He had thumbed his nose at Hades and tried to carry Sisyphus and his boulder over a mountaintop to care for Pam. Until the moment she died. It was time for Marco to care for himself.

Marco's first hip replacement was scheduled four weeks after Pam's funeral. Despite the drugs prescribed for his pain, Marco was in misery and admitted to a nursing home for pain control. He remained there after consecutive hip surgeries for convalescence and rehabilitation. Fortunately, a bed was available at the facility Johanna managed, which allowed her to attend to her father. Radio, television, and magazines did little to distract him. Johanna brought items from her parents' house to divert his attention. She advised his friends he would welcome company, an inclination he thought was debatable. Marco was engulfed by despair.

Soon after Marco was hospitalized, Johanna met and escorted me to his door. He sat on the side of his bed, ignored the football game on television, and stared out the window. Marco heard me walk in, turned, and winced. "Good afternoon—Ouch! Thanks for coming."

I glanced around the room, found a game box on a shelf, and deposited it on the table in front of Marco. "Mars, son of Juno and Jupiter! Prepare for battle."

The light returned to Marco's eyes. "Ahh. Ares, son of Hera and Zeus! We meet again. Have a seat."

Marco's and my mythic clashes in cribbage began, the playing cards our weapons and the pegs our chariots we raced around the perimeter of the game board. We conducted our contests in the nursing facility and at Marco's home while he recuperated. Our jubilation in victory and our distress in defeat were no less than those of our tennis court crusades of decades past.

Marco's depression eased. Johanna and Dean were solicitous. Marco's grandkids distracted him from his melancholia. The counsel from his doctor and advice from his support group were constructive. Our cribbage wars yielded no decisive victor. Marco still mourned, both for Pam and the loss of their plans to travel together.

"Marco. Why not take a trip?"

"Without Pam? By myself? I don't know. No. I couldn't do it. Not alone."

Memory of an old snapshot of two kids in tuxedos came to me. "I recall a war god who didn't let me give up on my senior prom. A war god who encouraged me to take a second shot. You, who washed my chariot, confident I'd find a new date. Which I did and got *two* proms out of the deal."

Marco smiled but shook his head.

I said, "You know I know that was nothing like what you've been through, what you're going through. But think! Think, for God's sake! My date did not become my lover or my wife. She was a friend. She became a better friend, to this day in fact, and someone Bev likes. You can find someone."

"I don't know..." Marco stared across the room at a photo of Pam and twisted the wedding band on his finger back and forth.

Like a new day rising, like the phoenix rising from the ashes, Pam returned. Marco and I prepared the playing cards and cribbage board for a rematch when someone knocked on the door and walked in. Johanna stood before her father. "Oh, Daddy..." Her face was flushed and tears flowed down her cheeks to her chin. "...I'm sorry...so sorry..."

Marco stood and embraced her. "What's wrong?"

Johannah sobbed and coughed. "It was so crazy at the end with Mom's funeral and you coming to the nursing home—"

"I know. I know. It was chaos."

"Remember when I brought you the cards and cribbage board?"

"Do I. Ares and Mars wouldn't have known what to do with themselves."

"You asked me to pack up Mom's things. I donated her clothes but had boxes filled up from her closet and chest-of-drawers. I meant to go through them but time slipped by. Maybe I was afraid... Last night, I started. I found a journal Mom kept. Did you know about it?"

"No. I thought she was writing her reports for work."

"Dad. I have to show you this. Please sit down." Marco complied. "I wish I'd found it sooner. Look at what she wrote. She dated this two years before she got sick."

Marco motioned me to look over his shoulder and we read.

My Darlings,

I woke up with a strange sensation and a memory from somewhere, from someplace. From a dream last night? I was summoned to depart for a mysterious place. And soon. But when? Everyone I knew, everything I did, everything I owned would stay behind. My sadness about this was outweighed by the light, the warmth, the comfort, the confidence, and the love that flowed through me.

I write this so you will know, and you read this because I have, well, died. Gone the way of all flesh. Kicked the bucket. Bought the farm. Gone belly up. Bitten the dust. Given up the ghost. Cashed in my chips. Croaked. I don't mean to be coarse. Please just smile! We all die. We go to a better place. We will meet again. Let us rejoice in that!

Until then, live your lives. Mourn but do not grieve for long. Heal, My Darlings. Laugh again. Know that I love you. Whether it be joy or whatever befalls you, I am with you.

Always.

Marco held his head with one hand and tapped his fingers on the table with the other. Johanna watched. I held my breath. "Your mother never had to have the last word. Until now. And she could be quite the trickster. Remember that Halloween? You were twelve, Dean was fifteen. She came out of the closet—"

I gasped. "What?"

Marco frowned at me. "I don't mean that, you knucklehead. It was Halloween for God's sake. Pam was in the closet and walked out dressed like the ugliest witch I'd ever seen. Scared the freaking daylights out of us. Then she tossed rubber rats at us."

"Eeeewwww!" Johanna did a fine imitation of her twelve-year-old self. "That *was* gross."

"And how about all those April Fool's Days?"

"I need to call Dean, Dad."

"Call him! Now!"

Marco and Johanna were paralyzed by laughter. I breathed again and watched my friend rising from the ashes.

Two summers later, I was at Marco's house. He babysat and relaxed in a lounge chair in his backyard with a newspaper while Johanna ran errands.

"How's Grandpa Mars doing today?"

"Splendid, sir. Would Ares like to crack that Jack Daniels you brought last time?"

"Sure. Hi, Lolo!" A seated mini-Johanna smiled at me, played with a truck with one hand, and grasped her grandfather's ankle with the other. "Looks like you're tied up, Marco. I'll fetch and serve."

"Just a finger-full for me, please."

"You got it."

I pulled two whiskey glasses from a cupboard, poured the Jack, and added ice cubes to cut the liquor. Before I returned outside, I toured the photo gallery in the living room. The family pictures of Johanna, Dean, Pam, and Marco endured. New ones continued to appear: Johanna and Dean with their future spouses. School portraits and candid photos of Marco's grandchildren. And, of course, the framed shots of Bella, Marco's companion for the past eighteen months: Bella and Marco in Rome. Athens. Mexico. Paris. Las Vegas. Niagara Falls. My friend had found his way around the world.

"Here you go, Marco."

"Thank you." Mars lifted his glass. "I propose a toast. To Bacchus for creating Jack Daniels. And to our friendship."

"Thanks. But wasn't Bacchus the god of wine? Not spirits?"

"Ahh." Mars clinked my glass. "Just testing you, Ares. Now drink up and—"

— cheer, cheer, cheer —

Marco sat upright and grabbed his glass with both hands. He was frantic as he looked about. "What was tha—?"

— cheer, cheer, cheer —

A cardinal flew from a tree, perched on another lounge chair across from us, and continued her whistle calls.

— cheer, cheer, cheer —

"Pam?"

The cardinal and Marco stared at each other. One minute, two minutes passed. The bird cocked her head, extended both wings, pirouetted on the top of the chair, and bowed.

Tears rolled down Marco's cheeks and framed his broad smile as he whispered, "Pam."

— cheer, cheer, cheer —

The cardinal flew away, ascended in a wide, sweeping spiral, up and up and up into the blue, and disappeared.

Night falls. Day rises. The two-step dance of our lives, the rhythm of our existences.

First, the Dark.

Last, the Light.

Echoes of what Marco and I were taught when we were children reverberated in my being. And, as Marco's friend and a witness to the miraculous, I came to believe what others, like Pam, somehow already knew and the rest of us hoped for.

"Heal, My Darlings" was inspired by the experiences of my friend, a gentleman and a scholar, a bit of a character, and a genuine hero. We have known each other since we were in middle school in the 1960s. His wife of over forty years suffered from and succumbed

to the sporadic form of Creutzfeldt-Jakob Disease (CJD) four years before this story was written. For more information about this terrible illness and ways to support afflicted patients and their families, please visit the Creutzfeldt-Jakob Disease Foundation at https://cjdfoundation.org/.

Douglas S. Levine is a physician, researcher, pharmaceutical R&D executive, and consultant who has authored 200 publications in clinical science journals and textbooks since 1976. Doug now applies his medical experience to fiction-writing and is over the moon to have his latest short story published in the 2023 ARIA anthology.

A FATHER'S ADVICE

by Risa Nyman

"Canada? Big mistake. You'll regret your choice,"
The father advises,
Emitting an exasperated exhale.

The son bellows,
Voice vibrating, cracking, hitching,
"I. have. principles. You don't understand me."

"Ha! Principles, you say. Bah. New age jumbo, Son,"
The father scoffs,
Belittling, dismissing.

Feet dancing an anxious side-to-side shuffle,
The son replies,
"Maybe I'm scared. Don't I have a right to be scared?"

"You shouldn't run, Boy. It's only a common draft. Be strong, and the
    time away will pass quickly,"
The father persuades,
Certain of this truth.

Pleading, wishing, questioning,
The son challenges,
"Stay? Be strong? Why?"

The father embraces,
Squeezing, squeezing his firstborn.
"You are no coward. You can do this. Others have."

"Maybe I am a coward! Consider that. It's my life. *My* life,"
The son mumbles,
Speaking into the father's chest.

Ending the intimate moment,
The father retorts,
"You'll be a bum in Canada, an aimless, wandering soul."

"Canada is my choice. I will wash dishes there,"
The son explains,
Longing for acceptance.

With eyes pinched over half-glasses,
The father scorns,
"Wash dishes? Pooh! That's not worthy of you."

The son struggles,
Desperate to break through.
"You are old, Father. You don't understand me."

"And you are young, Son, brimming with inexperience
  and misguided principles,"
The father emphasizes,
No longer the son's protector.

The son appeals,
Daring one final question.
"Aren't you scared for me, Father?"

"Trust me, Son. You'll return with a shiny future, ready for life,"
The father insists,
His weighty words ending the argument.

The son whispers,
Voice hollowed, shoulders slumped,
"Okay, no dodging. I promise. I trust you."

"Good boy. I'm proud of you,"
The father beams,
Slapping the son heartily on the back...

Dim lights, sentimental music, rose-scented candles.
The son sighs,
"Tell them to play some rap, Father. Amazing Grace is too sad."

The father rests his hand on the boy's cheek, no more backslapping.
The son wonders,
"Why is he so quiet? Too quiet, horribly quiet."

"Father, I know you're trying to rewrite the scene. Give it up,"
The son begs,
Wrecked by the persistent silence.

Recalling the end is torture, but it must be done.
The son describes,
"The rear. In the rear was safe, 'til the boom erupted
    in tall grass on my left."

The son remembers,
Shuddering at the recitation.
"Came fast. Dropped hard. I thought I went deaf,
    but my ears didn't hurt. Nothing hurt."

As a sympathetic monsoon streams into the crevices on Father's face,
The son confides,
"Enough, Father, my heart is already broken."

Changing the subject,
The son remarks,
"Love this silky, puffy pillow. Everything in 'Nam was rough and raw."

Now stooped and pale, the father's tongue finally shakes loose.
The father laments,
"I wish I could take back my advice, Son."

The son chuckles
at that ironic admission.
"Advice? No, it was more than advice. You said, 'Trust me.'"

The father gasps,
Weeping steadily, reminded of his words.
"'Trust me,' I said."

"I'm paying for this, Father. This isn't my Canadian homecoming."
With a wild wail echoing inside his heart,
The son cries.

The father straightens,
Swollen eyelids sinking, perhaps in prayer.
"I will not forgive myself for a day, an hour, a minute."

Before the heavy casket closes, forever shutting out the cold draft,
The son assures,
"Sorry, Father, this is beyond hard. For both of us."—

Risa Nyman is the author of two award-winning middle grade books, *Swallowed by a Secret* and *Spooked by a Suspicion*. Her first young adult novel, *Complicated Choices*, will be published in July 2023. These contemporary books deal with family issues, life changes, friendship, and loss.

MISCONCEPTIONS

by Joanne Perella

They were sitting in their favorite café next to the Connecticut River. Jen always liked looking down at the swirling current from their customary booth in a secluded nook by the window. It was her happy place, especially on an evening like this. The wind tossed the October leaves as they spiraled down in a muted rainbow of colors. With the trees stripped of leaves, the landscape would soon resemble early November. Jen dreaded the darkness of winter and tried to ignore the familiar pangs of melancholy and the deep sadness she knew the winter months would bring.

Paul's large strong hands held his wine glass and they both sipped in rhythm. It was nice, Jen thought, that they were always in rhythm. Suddenly, he slid his hand over hers in an uncharacteristic display of affection.

"Josh told me about an amazing trip he'd just heard about," Paul began. "One of the airlines is offering discount fares to Australia, and it includes a rental car, first class accommodations at a luxury suite, and even a couple of optional tours." He paused to take a breath, his eyes bright.

"You know that their seasons are reversed. So, it would be spring there and if we took a winter trip, we could avoid the awful winter months that you dread so much. Josh said to tell you right away because he and Sandy would like to book it with us. We could share the suite and expenses and it would be really affordable. We even have our passports ready!" Paul's smile seemed a little forced. His hand tightened on hers. His voice lowered into the sexy growl she loved so much.

"Of course, our bedroom will be away from theirs, so we can still have all the freedom we want, if you catch my drift." He leaned even closer. "Well, what do you say?"

Jen took a big gulp of wine and tried to compose herself. "Sounds like a dream trip to me," she began, abstractedly tracing the pattern around the base of the wine glass with her finger. She avoided his gaze. There was silence and then she cleared her throat.

"So, would this trip come out of the baby fund, or do you have a hidden stash of money somewhere?" she asked a little too brightly, taking another swallow of wine.

"Baby fund?" Paul looked confused and then he looked away quickly. "Okay. Yeah, what's wrong with using the baby fund? We can have a great adventure and then maybe the relaxation from the trip would erase all the anxiety that's causing us to not conceive right now. I think we really need this, Jen. At least I know *I* do."

Jen released her hand from his and took a deep breath. "Paul, you know we've been trying for over two years now and nothing has happened. Doctor Adams said we need to explore other possibilities. I think it's time for the in vitro or whatever they call it. I'm forty-one and not getting any younger. If we wait one more year until next spring, it will be even harder. We'll be older and more set in our ways."

She felt her composure beginning to slip. "I feel right now any eggs I have are shriveling up as we speak. Sure, the vacation sounds great for a couple who is carefree and has no obligations, but we're just prolonging the agony by putting the baby thing on the back burner." Her voice broke.

"What's so wrong with being carefree and having no obligations anyway?" Paul swallowed the rest of his wine and then continued. "You know, Jen, we really have it made. We're the envy of everyone I know.

My practice has taken off in the last couple of years, your art is finally starting to sell. We both love what we do; we have a house on a lake, lots of friends, our health, and no real problems. Don't you see how lucky we are? Some of my colleagues had a great life until the kids came along. Remember the Saltzmans? Their house used to be a showplace. Now you can't even go in the front door without tripping over one of those baby buggies, or whatever you call them. And they're always fighting. Patty's stuck at home with the baby. She's so tired they can't even enjoy a nice quiet dinner. Mike told me yesterday they haven't made love once since the baby was born." Paul signaled the waitress for refills and pushed back his dark hair, which had fallen into his eyes. The strain showed clearly in his face. They both stared at each other warily.

"What are you saying?" Paul's words were beginning to sink in. Jen squirmed in her seat and felt an unbearable tightness in her chest. "Are you giving up on our baby?"

"Listen, Jen." Paul shifted around in his seat, bent his head close to hers as he took a deep breath and continued, "Let's be honest here. This whole thing has been hard. Our lives for the last year, no, two years, have totally revolved around 'us' getting pregnant. Day in and day out, it's like we're both consumed with this crap. I can't even come home and have a normal conversation about something that happened at work anymore. It's like, oh, I've got to take my temperature to see if it's a 'good time.' Or, oh, please wait, I'll be ovulating tomorrow at 1:00 a.m. so we have to do it then. Save up your sperm, blah blah blah. I'll tell you, if I never hear the words 'ovary' or 'sperm' again, it wouldn't be too soon. I can't even order eggs for breakfast anymore because I am sick to death of talking about eggs!"

The waitress slipped two more glasses of wine on their table and bid a hasty retreat.

Jen's eyes were fixed on her napkin, decorated with brightly colored red and yellow leaves. She reached for her wine glass, took another long gulp, and her words spilled out in a rush.

"You think this is bad for *you*? How would you like to be the one that's doing all the work, taking temperatures, filling out the damn charts and running back and forth to the stupid fertility clinic? This is no picnic for me either. And you just sit around feeling like you're being neglected, ignoring the fact that maybe I'm the one who is stressed out and needs a little compassion. If you weren't so selfish, maybe I would have gotten pregnant by now!" Jen felt her face grow hot, but she wasn't finished. "I feel like I'm struggling with this mess all by myself. And now, all you can think about is escaping to Costa Rica or some damn place!" She felt the tears well in her eyes.

"Australia. Look Jen, I know it's been hard but that's the whole point. Let's take a break from all this, okay? Let's step back, go away for a while and rediscover ourselves, give ourselves a chance to rethink all this baby stuff." He sighed deeply. "I'm beginning to believe that having a baby is not all it's cracked up to be. At least for me," he added quietly.

"Great! So, what about me? What about us? Didn't we agree before we got married that we wanted children? Where the hell is this coming from anyway? So, you just change your mind and I'm supposed to say, oh yeah, I'll give up a huge part of my life and my dreams, because you don't feel like it anymore. I can't believe this! What's happening to you anyway? I never thought you were a quitter." Jen felt helpless as she watched her dreams slip away. "I can't imagine living the rest of my life without the hope of a family." Her voice cracked and tears spilled over her face.

"But *you* are my family. And no one is quitting; we'd just be rearranging our priorities." Paul sat up straight and downed his wine. His empty glass landed so heavily on the table that people stared. "Honestly, Jen, I can't believe you're happy about pumping your body full of these horrible hormones every week either!" Paul looked around and lowered his voice as he continued.

"Look, why can't it be just you and me, like it was in the beginning, like it was when we got married? What's wrong with that? I can be happy with just us. I married you so we could have just us, all the time. I guess I've had a change of heart because I want my life back. I want our life back; I miss you. Maybe I just liked our life too much the way it was. And I can't believe you didn't like it too." Paul took both her hands in his. His blue eyes were serious, the same eyes she had hoped their children would have.

"Think about it, Jen. We don't need to be one of those couples lugging baby stuff around, calling each other Mommy and Daddy and all that annoying baby talk, with rug rats running rampant around the house destroying all our stuff. We can have a great life, jetting off to exotic places whenever we want, while our stressed-out friends are up all night with their damn 3:00 a.m. feedings and terrible two tantrums. The way I see it, well, we don't need to have a baby to feel fulfilled. We don't have to fall into that trap." He squeezed her hands tightly. "We're both way too smart for that."

Jen tore her shaking hands away quickly. "Sure, I've been really smart," she spat angrily. "Really, really smart, huh? Seems like I've been deluding myself all along, convincing myself that my partner, my soul mate, my husband, was on the same page as I was. Turns out, he wants no part of the tough stuff. He only wants smooth clear sailing, and if a storm looms ahead, he's ready to bail out! Yeah, when the going gets tough, the tough get going, huh? Right, well, that's what I'm going to do. I'm going!"

She pulled herself up and the chair scraped behind her, almost tipping over. Angrily, she managed to grab her purse and headed to the door. She couldn't look at Paul's face. He didn't try to stop her. Jen managed to keep her composure until the door slammed behind her.

Outside, her tears spilled, and she shook with fear. Menacing clouds skittered quickly across the sky. Above the raging river the wind picked up; her world was now a very dark place.

Joanne Perella is a freelance writer and has been writing for as long as she can remember. Her essays have been published in previous ARIA anthologies. She has completed her first novel, *Vanishing Act,* and is currently seeking a publisher. Besides writing, she spends her time photographing landscapes, traveling, cooking and selling real estate.

HER PALE GREEN EYES

by Guy Natelli

Does the wind call your name?
Will it wrench you from my heart, from our bed?
Aloft on gossamer wings,
Will your pale green eyes disappear from view?

The snow falls and covers the straw-colored grass like a white blanket.
The full moon rises and illuminates the landscape with its brilliant glow,
Casting shadows about you, framing you,
Trying to capture you for his own,
As your soft golden hair encircles your face.

Does the wind call your name?
Will it summon you from my heart, from our bed?
Will your pale green eyes vanish from my sight?

The long shadows stretch across the landscape on the glistening snow.
Even nature cannot compare to what I see in your beautiful pale green
    eyes,
But your soul lies deep...
                   and is surrounded by a thousand ghosts.
Try as I might I fear I cannot reach your heart,
As I lean over the precipice that is your past.

Does the wind call your name?
Will it draw you from my heart, from our bed?
Will your pale green eyes disappear from view?

You tell me stories that stab at my heart.
You tell me of things that crush my soul.
You tell me of sweet pale green eyes that have seen too much.

Your soul lies deep...
and is surrounded by a thousand ghosts.
Try as I might I fear I cannot reach your tender heart.
As I lean over the precipice that is your past,
I weep for your lost innocence.

Does the wind call your name?
Will it whisk you away from my heart, from our bed?
Will your pale green eyes fade from view?

Look into my eyes as I look into yours,
As I gaze upon your face framed by your soft golden hair.
My soul laid bare, my heart exposed –
                                                You touch me.
I try to touch you but your soul lies so deep,
And it is surrounded by a thousand dreadful ghosts.
Try as I might, I fear I can never reach you.

Does the wind call your name?
Does it summon you?
Does it hold sway over your heart and your soul?
Will it lure you from my heart, from our bed?
Or will the vine that is us wither,
And will you choose to leave of your own accord?
Am I to become just one... more... ghost?
Do I have a chance?
Or will your gentle pale green eyes disappear from view?

        Forever.

Guy Natelli discovered the joy of storytelling later in life, and his writing has appeared in previous anthologies. He serves ARIA as treasurer, and coordinates its "Lively Literati" event, where storytellers engage their audience with reflections and poetry.

DECEMBER 13

by Jodi L. Leffingwell

The path to the church steps was bursting with people, reporters, and mourners. It was chaotic, surreal, somber, and bleak. Reporters frantically tried to take pictures of my grandparents and parents as they walked into the church, trying to catch a glimpse of the beautiful casket my grandmother had so frantically and stoically chosen. A reporter edged in too close, only to be met by the fist of my uncle, who swiftly reacted to such a gross intrusion on our family as they tried to walk into the funeral. Hundreds of people poured inside to mourn the most indescribable, incandescent, and beautiful light extinguished in such a tragic way. It was just days until Christmas, yet there was no festive feeling. It was as if the sun had not risen, and we had been walking in darkness since that phone call just a few short days before, on December 13. The church procession to the cemetery was extensive, with everyone paying their last respects. The line of cars was a tribute to our family but, most importantly, a tribute to the beautiful soul that did so much more than anyone ever knew. She did so much more than any newspaper reported. They didn't know what truly happened that cold night which led us to these church steps and St. Mary's Cemetery just days before Christmas.

December 13. December 13, 1977. It is a day that will be forever emblazoned on our hearts. It is a day that changed the course of our family's history. It is a day that changed the trajectory of all of us, even those who had not been born yet. Jacqueline Luiza Botelho was born on July 17, 1957, to my grandparents, Olga and Gildo. She was the youngest child of three siblings, the youngest and the only daughter. Jackie was the sunshine in everyone's darkness. She grew up in the small town of Bristol, Rhode Island, was of Portuguese descent, and was a member of an extremely community-focused, socially active family. We called her Jackie. Jackie went to St. Elizabeth's School, which was attached to the family parish, and then she went off to Fatima High School, another parochial school in the area.

From an early age, Jackie was popular, not only within our extensive Portuguese family and friends but with all she encountered. She had a circle of friends, boyfriends, and family members who adored her, wanted to be around her, and with whom she enjoyed spending her time. Jackie wasn't someone you could forget.

When I came into the picture, Jackie was already fifteen years old and in high school.

I quickly became her sidekick, accompanying her wherever she let me go. She was one of my favorite humans. It didn't hurt that I was a bit of her doppelganger. Jackie was special. She wasn't your ordinary, run-of-the-mill girl. She was my best friend, my confidante, and I was her super young and rambunctious niece who always wanted to be with her. She and her presence influenced the most formative experiences of my early childhood. She was responsible for my first public singing appearance at three years old at Fatima High School: two pigtails, one microphone, and my jumper hiked up so high that you could see my unmentionables and ruffles underneath. I was her co-pilot on many adventures in the pea-green Grand Prix with the white leather seats in the days when you could sit in the front seat without a seatbelt. She and her college boyfriend, Greg, gave me my first dog, whom we appropriately named Snoopy. Yet, these descriptions do not do her justice, nor reflect the impact she had on all she encountered. Friends surrounded her, and she always had a boyfriend. Even to this day, friends and old boyfriends alike express their love for her wistfully, and the mention of her name evokes tears from many who I have spoken with in the years since December 13, 1977.

I remember being sad when Jackie graduated from Fatima High School and moved away to college, as she would not be at Gram and Gramp's house every day, which happened to be right down the street from our house. Gram said PC was pretty close, and Jackie would be home on weekends. Life would be pretty much the same for us as a family. Jackie was the first member of our immediate family to attend college, a title that would be handed down to me after December 13.

Jackie took college by storm. She was not one to sit back and watch. She tried out for the Providence College Friars basketball cheerleaders and made it on the team. We all quickly became basketball fans, and I can tell you that I loved her uniform. I wanted one. Her uniform was black and white with a PC embroidered on the chest, and black-and-white saddle shoes. She had black-and-white pom poms, which I have kept to this day. We loved watching her more than the game itself. She made it into the paper a few times, cheering at half-time center court or on the sidelines, pom poms swinging high above her head, eyes twinkling. We still have all of the clippings.

Jackie also had a deep love for community service. She lived the "service above self" mentality. She was raised to understand that community service and activism were part of our every day and that we should always do whatever we could to help those around us. Whether Jackie served soup at a church feast, volunteered at her alma mater, Fatima High School, coached the cheerleaders, or worked with kids, it gave her joy. That sparkle in her eye shone brightly when she was working in the service of others, so much so that it became her calling. As Jackie entered her junior year of college, she made a difficult decision. She decided to leave the PC cheerleading squad and concentrate on her social service major. Jackie was also the resident assistant on the fourth floor of Aquinas Hall, one of the largest female dormitories on campus. She had many first- and second-year students in her charge, and she lived her role and commitment to service above self.

No one could have known it would happen. No one could have anticipated. There was such a festive feeling in the dorm. The halls, doors, and walls were all decked for Christmas, as there was a holiday decorating contest. It was the week leading to final exams, and everyone was in full-on study mode. There were just a few more days before break. Jackie loved the Christmas season and everything about it. She loved coming home for Christmas, even though she wasn't far away, and she *loved* Christmas Eve. Christmas Eve at my grandparents' house was quite the extravaganza, complete with an open house, musicians, instruments, dancing, and a lot of singing. Everyone would play an instrument—Gram on the accordion, Dad on the guitar, and Jackie and I got the triangle. We would host hundreds of people who would stop in for food, drink, and entertainment. We would have to wait until midnight, after all the guests had left, to open gifts. Not an easy feat for her or me.

There was an overwhelming sense of anticipation in the air during that second week of December, and students were in the throes of studying for finals. To top it off, it was beginning to look a lot like Christmas on campus, as Jack Frost had delivered a blanket of snow, and now the halls were decked. It was enough to get the students away from their desks and out to the quad for a good old-fashioned snowball fight. It was just the break they needed from the rigors of prepping for exams. There were many accounts of what happened next, but I will share with you what I know to be true. Even as I type these words, I get that knot in the pit of my stomach, knowing what is to come.

As you may imagine, after the snowball fights on the quad, the girls were covered in snow, their clothing wet. They returned to the dorm to finish the night studying. There were only a few short days before they would all be leaving for Christmas. Jackie was also back in the dorm, in her room. Her boyfriend Greg had come to visit. There were parietals at Providence College so the boys could visit, but they had to be out of the dorm by the designated time. The security guards would phone the girl's room to ensure the expedient exit of the boys. Jackie was very uneasy that night for no reason. She could not explain why. It may have been the anxiety of final exams, or was it? She was so uneasy that she asked her boyfriend to stay with her until she fell asleep.

They say that time moves in slow motion when experiencing a tragedy. When confronted with paralyzing trauma, a small amount of time can feel like an eternity. That time was approximately 2:57am to 3:39am on December 13, 1977. The smell of smoke began to permeate the fourth-floor halls, with flames quickly taking hold of the hallways. To this day there is a question as to whether the fire began from a hairdryer propped up to dry clothes after the snowball fight, or a light that was shining on a creche in the Christmas display. Those beautiful Christmas decorations swiftly became an accelerant of the fire. Witnesses say that you could hear the girls' screams as some realized they were trapped in their rooms with no exit. There was no sprinkler system, even though the building had passed an inspection by the Providence Fire Department not long before.

Jackie acted, doing her best to get everyone out of the building. She called each girl by name as she navigated the smoke and the flames, reassuring all that the fire department would be there. No time to think, only time to react. I can't even imagine the fear in the minds of those poor women.

Outside the building, chaos ensued, with fire, police, students, college personnel, and media gathering. Students fought back against the media, who tried to invade the area to take photos of the girls as they clung to the windows, trying to escape the fourth floor.

Jackie had managed to exit the building and, in her role as a resident assistant, went diligently through her list to account for all the girls in her charge. She was seen and identified outside the building by several others. When going through her list, she noticed girls missing. I cannot tell you how she made it back into the burning building without being noticed. In all the commotion, we can assume that there was too much going on, and no one caught sight of her. However, we know she made it back in. Knowing Jackie, I would have expected nothing less. The room where the fire started had three girls in it. Two of those women, so stricken with fear, jumped to their death out the fourth-floor window. The third waited and was rescued just three minutes later by the firefighters.

Jackie had made it to the two girls she was missing and was headed toward the exits when the smoke overtook her and the two girls. Fire and rescue found her on the floor, linked arm-in-arm with the other two girls. When found, Jackie was barely breathing and was quickly brought by ambulance to Roger Williams Hospital. While she made it out of the building alive, the Lord called her home en route to the hospital. Her cause of death was smoke inhalation. She had one little singe mark on her forehead above her eyebrow. The two beautiful girls that she tried so desperately to save also perished.

A makeshift morgue was set up in Aquinas Chapel for those who did not survive. There were six women already in that morgue. Jackie was the seventh victim, and there would be more.

When the phone rings in the middle of the night, even to this day, I feel sick to my stomach. The aftermath would change the trajectory of our lives permanently. I don't know who called, although I remember hearing the message came from Father Peterson, the college president. It was just ten days before Christmas, and my grandparents and parents, uncle, and aunt would now have to identify her body. She was our world. She was the apple of my grandfather's eye, his only daughter, irreplaceable. My grandmother was stoic yet inconsolable, as were my dad and my uncle. How could this have happened? She didn't deserve to die.

The loss of a child incites grief and pain that breaks you from the inside. The coming days would not be easy for my family as we prepared to say goodbye to Jackie. The media would not leave us alone. They tried at every turn to speak to any of our family members to get them to say something about what happened. They camped outside the house, the funeral home, and the church, waiting for an opportunity. I watched my family breaking, even though they tried to shield me from it.

In the pain and despair of grief, it becomes hard to justify our faith in anything or find solace, comfort, or understanding. Yet, my grandparents were steadfast in their belief that Jackie's death was not in vain. She was trying to save the lives of others. She was living her purpose of service above herself, even if that meant we lost her. So much so that to honor Jackie, we still had our usual Christmas celebration that year. We kept things as Jackie would have wanted, even though everyone was struggling with grief.

In the months and years that followed, my grandparents rallied with several parents of the other girls that we lost in the fire, to lobby for national fire regulations in college dormitories. They had offsite meetings and put together programs and processes that would later be implemented in college dormitories across the country. Still, we never really knew Jackie's impact on people until we were invited back to the college for the 25th anniversary of the fire. My grandparents were still living, and we all returned to a mass in the chapel and dinner to commemorate and honor the memories of all the girls. There were hundreds and hundreds of people at this event. Speakers shared their stories and memories of the girls, but something else happened.

As we were sitting at our table, I noticed a line of women forming to the left of my grandmother. "Are you Mrs. Botelho, Jackie's mom?" the woman said. My grandmother nodded. One after the other, they each thanked my grandmother and thanked Jackie for saving their lives. "We wouldn't be here if it wasn't for Jackie." None of us could hold it together. While we had gotten notes over the years, we had never heard directly from the survivors.

It has been 46 years since that December 13. There is not a day that goes by when I don't look at Jackie's picture, think of her, or wish that my siblings had gotten to know her. There is not a moment where I don't wonder if our lives would be different if she had survived. I look like her, and I have been approached many times by people who say, "Are you related to Jackie?" I always happily say yes. Just last night, someone came to my table in a restaurant and asked if I am related to

Jackie, saying, "You have the same sparkle in your eye as she did." My reply? "That is the best compliment you could ever give me." I do know that she has become a role model, namesake, and guardian angel for so many. She was a hero, my hero, and her story is a legacy to be preserved and passed on.

Jodi L. Leffingwell Ed. D is an award-winning author and thought leader focusing on women's roles and rights in leadership. Jodi resides by the water in Rhode Island, and her favorite role is being mom to Abigale and Aubrey and wife to husband Eric.

PROJECT SAVE POINT

by Tim Baird

"A1, come in," the man spoke into the microphone. He paused for a moment, allowing himself a much-needed deep breath before letting his anxious thoughts get the best of him. "A1, this is A2, come in." Another pause. "I repeat, A1, come in."

Static.

"Commander Cavill, this is Commander Zahn, please come in."

Again, static filled the air. This wasn't entirely unusual given the often-extreme environments within which they found themselves, but the pilot knew that there shouldn't have been any major concerns for loss of signal on this mission. The sky was cloudless and there was little between them and their cluster of dedicated satellites providing weather intel and communication relays. An LOS was the last thing he was worried about.

Looking down at the control panel before him, the man was about to press the button on the microphone once more when the speaker gurgled to life.

"Cavill to Zahn, sorry about that," the voice of Commander Cavill called out. "Things were a little dicey back there, but we're out and in one piece. En route to the rendezvous point. ETA...twenty minutes."

"Roger, Commander," Zahn replied. "A2 to pull back and await your arrival. We'll leave the light on for you."

Hanging the microphone on its hanger, Zahn leaned back in the chair of his Little Bird and let out a breath. He immediately felt the stress from the past few minutes release from his body, carried away by the air that slowly escaped his lungs. This wasn't their first rodeo, not by far, but it had been a while since they'd run into any serious trouble, and he was growing comfortably used to the idea.

"Everything alright, sir?" the voice said from the seat beside him.

Zahn looked to the seaman and sighed. "I think so, Henry, I think so. Well—I hope so. I had expected him to radio in a little while ago, so this delay, coupled with the dangerous nature of our mission, just made me worry a little."

He gave the man a pat on the shoulder.

"What do you say we get this bird in the air and meet up with the other team on their way back to the sub?"

"Yes, sir," Gilroy replied crisply.

Both men took their controls and breathed life into the tiny craft. Within moments, the two humans and their mechanical counterpart were in the air and heading back to the USS Sanders, eager to learn what had just happened.

*

"We got friggin set up, that's what happened!" the man bellowed.

The others in the room recoiled at the outburst, but the looks on their faces spoke deeply of compassion. From the man's accounts, they had barely made it out alive.

The officer before him, Captain Anthony Filoni, held up his hands. "Commander Cavill, please, let's sit back down and start from the beginning, alright?"

As the leader of this band of hooligans and senior officer on board both the Sanders and the Sagan, it was his job to keep everything running smoothly and his people in good spirits. He motioned to the empty chairs around the small table set up at the bridge. Normally, a table and chairs could have never fit in this area on a Columbia Class nuclear submarine, but the USS Sanders had been extensively modified to run with a smaller crew enjoying larger common spaces. The nature of their work demanded the comfort and mental health of the crew to warrant some sacrifices of extraneous equipment. They'd all be much more comfortable after being picked up by the Sagan and back in space where they had more room.

Taking his seat, the captain looked over his shoulder at the young man by the doorway. "Seaman Gilroy, would you mind wrangling coffees for everyone? Maybe some snacks, too? This might be a while."

"Yes, sir, coming right up," the seaman said, ducking through the portal and disappearing beyond. The captain felt bad ordering a member of his crew off to do menial tasks which he normally would have done himself, but he knew that Cavill needed something good in his system before he popped.

His head resting on his hands, Commander Cavill finally looked up. Taking a deep breath, he continued, albeit with a more focused, calm demeanor.

"I'm sorry for my outburst, sir, it's just—"

"No apologies necessary, Liam, I get it."

The use of his first name sank in with the commander. He wasn't just giving a mission report to his superior officer, he was talking to a friend.

"Thank you, sir," he resumed. "As planned, we took the two helicopters out on November 3, 1938. That gave us several days to fly in through the countryside to just outside Paris, hide the choppers in the woods where they hopefully wouldn't be seen, and travel into the city by foot to avoid any unwanted attention. We'd then find Herschel Grynszpan and try to talk him out of it. It took us a little longer than expected, but we finally found the target on the morning of November 7, just hours before he was slated to walk into the embassy and shoot Ernst vom Rath."

The room was dead quiet. Nobody was sure how effective this mission would have been but few had concerns over the ease of its execution.

Compared to some of their other plots, this should have been a slam dunk.

"And how did that go?" Captain Filoni asked, softly.

"How do you think it went?" Mercer barked out. Filoni looked to the woman, his eyes moving downward and focusing on the bloody stains of her coveralls.

Cavill glared at the young recruit but restrained himself. "Ensign Mercer, please help Gilroy with the coffee, will ya?"

The ensign looked like she was going to say something else, but closed her mouth, took a breath, and left the room. The outburst might not have been tolerated in the days of old, but these weren't common times, and this wasn't the traditional military.

"My apologies, sir," Cavill began. "Things were pretty hairy back there and we both got banged up. She just needs a little R&R and she'll be operational again."

Filoni held up an understanding hand. "Of course. Of course. We all could at this point. As you were saying..."

"Right," Cavill said, pausing. His eyes darted across the floor as his mind raced through the details of the past several days. "So, we tailed Grynszpan from his apartment to a café where he was enjoying his morning meal. Mercer and I followed him in from a distance and took an adjacent table. We were running low on rations and needed to refuel anyway, so we ate breakfast while talking loudly enough for him to overhear."

"What did you talk about?" Filoni asked.

"Well, we knew what was on the young man's mind, right?" Cavill said, leading the other man along in his thinking. "And we knew what he was gearing up to do, well, at least historically speaking. So, we started talking about how much we hated the Nazi party and how we wished that there was something that could be done. It wasn't until we openly talked about 'taking someone out' that he quietly slid his chair over and asked to join us.

"One thing led to another, and next thing you know, he's spilling

273

the beans about his parents being captured and how much he hates the Nazi party. He tells us what he would do if he had a gun and was within range of one of those bastards."

Hearing footsteps approach, both men turned and gratefully accepted the proffered mugs from the seaman and ensign. Filoni held his, calmly waiting for the other man, while Cavill cupped it with both hands and quickly downed the first half in one gulp.

"Sit and relax for a few, but grab some more when you get a chance, please," Filoni whispered to Seaman Gilroy, giving him an appreciative nod of his head. This was going to take a while.

The debriefing went long into the night. In the end, the event played out exactly as it had the first time around. Even with their attempted meddling, some things were just meant to happen. Grynszpan still killed the diplomat, and the Nazis still used it as an excuse to carry out their terror on Kristallnacht...the team had put in all that hard work and planning for nothing.

By the time the team had brought Captain Filoni up to speed with the key details, everyone in the room was fighting to keep their eyelids up. Seeing the general status of the assembled crew, the captain dismissed them and requested a deeper dive tomorrow after they all had a chance to rest up. There was no point in continuing this evening.

*

Early the next morning, on the other side of the ship, Commander Cavill padded along the corridor leading to the stern. Waking earlier than normal and unable to fall back asleep, he decided to grab a cup of tea and head to one of his favorite hiding spots. Reaching the end of the walkway and finding himself at the base of a short ladder, he paused and took a long sip from his lukewarm raspberry green tea. He hated to drink hot drinks and would only touch the tea after it had cooled down enough. Reaching up as high as he could, he placed the paper cup on top of the landing and climbed up the five rungs to the next level.

Looking down to take his cup, he stopped and gazed around, stupefied as to why he couldn't find it. "Where did the dang thing go?"

"Good morning, sir," a voice whispered from the dark. A hand reached out from the shadows bearing the missing cup of tea.

"Jesus H. Tap Danc—"

"Sorry, sir!" Gilroy blurted out, moving forward, his face appearing in the pale starlight. "I like to come up here sometimes to think and be alone. I didn't know that you couldn't see me."

Catching his breath, Cavill gripped the rail tightly, amazed that he hadn't fallen backwards with that momentary panic attack. Finishing his climb, he stepped up onto the landing. Taking the cup from Gilroy as his eyes adjusted to the gloomy shadows of the gunnery pod, he moved to sit down.

"Oh, sir!" Gilroy stammered, moving to the side. "Please, have the chair."

Cavill waved him off. "You were here first, seaman. It's all yours," he said, taking a sip. "Thank you all the same, though."

Settling into the form-hugging leather chair, Seaman Gilroy leaned back and stared up at the glass canopy overhead.

"Thank you, sir," he began. "I love coming up here early in the morning while the ship is still quiet. It's my favorite spot to just sit back, relax, and look out into the galaxy. Sitting here in the dorsal gunner's seat, you can see the rest of the Milky Way, beckoning you to come and explore."

Cavill leaned his head back against the wall panel. Taking another sip of his tea, he listened in reverence to the innocent awe pouring from the seaman's words. With everything going on in his head, trying to balance the safety of his crew and the fate of the human race, he often forgot to simply enjoy the wondrous views afforded them as they soared through the vacuum.

"Ooh!" Gilroy said, whistling. "Check this out, Commander. You can see the new hab cluster they're building on the far side of the Moon."

Cavill sat there, grinning as he watched the younger man. His enthusiasm for something so old and technically boring to the commander reminded the officer why they were doing all of this in the first place.

Looking back, Gilroy saw the other man smiling up at him. "What is it?" he said, sheepishly. "There's food on my face again, isn't there?" He wiped his lips and cheeks with his hands, looking into the darkened glass of the canopy to find a reflective surface.

Laughing, Cavill took another sip and set the cup down on the deck beside him. "No, not at all, seaman. At ease, that's an order."

Gilroy stopped fussing as he looked back to the commander but couldn't help taking another glance at the glass. "Is everything alright, sir?"

"Yes, quite, actually," Cavill resumed. "I just sometimes forget how much younger you are than the rest of us and how a lot of this is still new and exciting to you. Most of us have been doing this for so long that we tend to forget we're living in a world that was once the dreams of science fiction to us growing up. Have you ever even been planet-side? I mean, post-Event?"

"No, sir," Gilroy said wistfully. "I was born afterwards on the McAuliffe Station in low orbit. I've had my boots on the ground a bunch of times now with our crew, but never in the present timeline."

The two men fell silent, each looking away from the other, their thoughts adrift. Gilroy cleared his throat.

"How did you all come together, sir," he began. "If you don't mind me asking. I've heard stories here and there about things were pre-Event, but very little about how it all went down for you personally. But like, what happened to you and how did you find yourself in this current role?"

The commander leaned his head forward and let out a slow whistle. "That's quite a mouthful. How much time do you have?"

Both men chuckled for the briefest of moments and drifted off to silence. Gilroy picked at a scab on his arm, afraid that he had gone too far asking so much in one shot, and looked for a mental out. Cavill took a deep breath, afraid to dive back into memories, which like the scab on Gilroy's arm, would probably never fully heal.

"Where to begin? Where to begin..." Cavill said, his eyes darting around the canopy, trying to find something real to anchor himself to as he ventured into painful territory. "Well, for me, grad school, I guess. I was doing my post-doc work at Caltech and was affiliated with a team at JPL."

"JPL?" Gilroy asked. "What's that? It sounds familiar but I can't place the name."

"Yeah, that's right, you might not know," Cavill said, sighing. "Many of them were lost early on as the enemy saw their knowledge and technical capabilities as valuable assets to wipe out and deny our forces." He paused. "Those who survived wound up on Lunar Base Aldrin but dropped off the radar soon after. They mostly work in secret now on government projects to minimize anyone finding out where they are located."

"Do you know where they are now?" Gilroy asked, excitedly.

"I can neither confirm nor deny that."

Gilroy bellowed out laughing but quickly trailed off as he looked into the cold stare of the commander's eyes. He wasn't kidding.

"Sorry," Gilroy murmured, straightening up in his seat.

The commander waved it off. "Anyway, I was working alongside Dr. Vincent, who was just Katie at the time as she hadn't defended her thesis yet, when something strange happened to one of our satellites."

"What happened?"

"It was the summer of 2040, and we had just moved our fleet of satellites into their positions around the Sun. We wanted to gather data from the other side of the Sun as we normally can't with traditional means, so we parked relay comsats at L4 and L5, with our main satellite at L3. That way, whatever the satellite at L3 saw, we'd have a redundant means to receive the transmissions back on Earth.

"Well, shortly after we had everything in place and were able to establish a link, we lost contact with the satellite. After failing to recover from the LOS for a week, we sent the L4 unit into orbit around the Sun to see what happened at L3. Several days later, it arrived to find nothing waiting for it."

"The satellite was destroyed?"

"Not destroyed," Cavill replied dryly. "Just gone. Completely gone with absolutely no trace to be found. It was like it had never existed."

"Whoa."

"Yeah, I know," the commander agreed, shaking his head. "We left the original L4 satellite parked at L3, established a link to L5, and were just about to start gathering data, when—"

"Aliens."

"What?"

"Aliens came and took the satellite, didn't they?" Gilroy probed, earnestly.

"Oh, no," Cavill retorted, chuckling. "Aliens, Gilroy? Don't be silly. You know that we didn't have a real first contact until 2053."

"Oh, right," Gilroy returned, dismayed. "Wait! What about that thing in 2051?"

"That was never confirmed," Cavill said, with a wink. "At least officially."

The seaman beamed, happy that he finally got some sliver of secret knowledge out of the older man.

"Anyway, back to the story," Cavill declared, putting the tale back on course before they drifted too far off on another tangent, as he was well known to do. "After talking amongst some of our peers in the academic circle, we found out that another team of researchers at JPL had discovered wreckage of a similar-sounding satellite in the vicinity of L3 almost three years prior to its disappearance.

"We were obviously skeptical, because we had done a tremendously thorough background investigation prior to starting our work and had never heard of another team attempting anything like ours. It was half the reason why we thought to do it in the first place, just to be the first ones to do it! But, sure as heck, there in the 2037 edition of 'The Astrophysical Journal' was a paper published about their find."

Gilroy stared back at the man, mouth agape.

"Katie and I reached out to their team and promised them an

interesting story if they'd join us for dinner sometime. We all met up in L.A. one Saturday night to swap stories and share notes. It was obviously a little more expensive than staying in Pasadena, but we were trying to impress them. Little did we know that they would completely one-up us by bringing show and tell items."

"What did they bring?" Gilroy asked, leaning in closer.

"As we were waiting for drinks to come, one of their scientists opened his messenger bag and pulled out a chunk of titanium sheet metal. Katie and I looked at each other excitedly, as we both immediately recognized it. I eagerly reached out and took the piece of charred metal from the gentleman, turned it over, and there on the underside were the signatures from me, Katie, and the rest of our team. It was the heat shield that went around the computer from our missing satellite."

Gilroy gasped.

"They explained that they had more pieces back at their lab but were afraid to bring them given that some of the components were still emitting residual gamma radiation and were in containment units.

"So, after wolfing down our food while we peppered them with thousands of questions, we all ventured over to their lab to see the parts," Cavill continued. He took a deep breath before resuming, his hands shaking. "It wasn't much to see as the sat had presumably impacted with some unknown orbiting body, but it was definitely recognizable as one of our babies."

Commander Cavill looked up toward the canopy overhead. He didn't say anything for a few moments as his unfocused eyes stared out into the void.

Nearly jumping out of his seat with excitement, Gilroy broke the silence. "So, what the heck happened? How did your satellite get into their lab all smashed up and stuff?"

Turning back to the seaman, Cavill blinked away the fog covering his pupils and took a deep breath. "From what we could tell, especially thanks to the three-plus years of study that they had already put into it, the radioisotope thermoelectric generator had ruptured and detonated as the satellite put a load on its system. Why it had completely disappeared, but then turned up years earlier, none of us had any clue.

"That is, until we had our eureka moment one day. While narrowing the list of variables that differentiated our event from any normal artificial body in space, we found ourselves looking at two potential smoking guns. One was the location, as very little exploration or testing of any kind had ever occurred at L3. The other was the radiation spike. There's still so little that we understand about radiation given its inherent danger in testing, so we left that one on the whiteboard as a matter of concern.

"So, we began to experiment. We sent out simplified probes to the different LaGrange points around the Sun and nearby locations. We monitored various visual and auditory spectrums to pick up anything that might have caused the disappearance. We used the same materials with the same drive systems and everything... and nothing happened. That is, until Kelso convinced us to circle back to the radiation."

Gilroy continued to stare in awe. "I love this stuff! I never got to play with anything radioactive in school. What did you do?"

And for good reason, Cavill thought. In a post-Event world, it was universally understood that nuclear weapons, most forms of nuclear energy, and pretty much all forms of harmful radiation were off the syllabus in what few schools remained. The consensus was that if humanity collaboratively forgot the knowledge, it just might go away on its own, never to be seen again.

"We started playing with different types and magnitudes of radiation which could have been found naturally in that area, as well as anything introduced by the presence of the satellite," Cavill answered. "It took a while and several complete failures, but the team was eventually able to duplicate the exact radiation levels released by the damaged RTG. We rigged up an emitter floated it out to L3, and—"

"*It disappeared!*"

Cavill sighed and blinked a few times. "Yes, it disappeared. Man, you suck at listening to stories."

"I'm sorry!" Gilroy exclaimed. "But you're dragging this out forever. Get to the good deets!"

"Alright, alright, but only because I haven't fully woken up yet and want another cup of tea," Cavill conceded. "The probe ended up going back the exact same number of years. We literally turned around and found our new probe sitting next to the other debris labeled with a respective change in date. Katie and I were surprised, but the JPL team was confused as to why we didn't know about it. They swore that they had already reviewed it with us. And that's when it hit us."

"You guys had invented—"

"Time travel!" The commander blurted out, not to be outdone. "Ha! Beat ya to it. Yes, we were sending items back in time. We couldn't believe it and spent the next year continuing to test it in secret before even dreaming of publishing our work. It was literally science fiction and we just assumed that the scientific community, let alone the whole world, would call us crazy if we weren't 100% correct in our findings. And we were just about to publish our work when it happened..."

"The Event?"

"Yep...the Event," Cavill said, sinking back into the wall. "There was a lot of confusion at first and we still don't really know for sure who fired first, but the dark, cool atmosphere of that night was suddenly filled with multiple ICBMs heading in different directions. They think that North Korea fired first, some say it was the Russians, but regardless, we had Patriot missiles skyward within moments. But, there were just too many to intercept. After the first one hit Minot... well, we countered hard.

"L.A. ended up getting hit with five different strikes a few minutes later and took out most of the surrounding area, including JPL and Caltech. All of our colleagues were just...gone. Katie, Kelso, and I were lucky enough to be on a hiking trip in western Colorado at the time and managed to be far enough away from the strike on Cheyenne Mountain. But our homes, our friends, everything that we ever knew... was gone."

Gilroy, apt to crack a joke during an awkward conversation, was silent.

"As the dust was still settling, many of us in or connected to space exploration covertly secured passage to the Moon or Mars," Cavill continued. "We spent a few months sitting on our new discovery while we coped with what we had just lost, but ultimately Katie and I decided to continue with our research. We didn't have any solid funding given that the world as we knew it had literally just ended, but we were able to salvage spare parts and cobble together our own materials. Using lightweight launch systems from the lunar surface and finding the corresponding data in the Internet archives, we found that the magnitude of radiation directly correlated to how far back in time the unit would travel. We experimented with this for a while and got pretty good at dialing in just the right ratio of rads to material density to get when we were aiming for. Park something in L3, emit a defined level of gamma radiation, and poof! You go back in time. And if you're in the same location twenty-two days later, then you'll emerge back at the same physical location at the original time of departure. And no, we don't know why it's twenty-two. Not yet, at least.

"As you can probably tell, we don't fully understand how this phenomenon works. If it wasn't for most of life being wiped out on Earth, we wouldn't normally take such risks like we do now without exhaustive unmanned testing. But, as you've figured out these past few months stationed aboard the Sagan, we don't have very many options aside from completely restarting humanity from scratch. That's why we document every miniscule thing we do and continue to review every scrap of information that we can get our hands on.

"Dr. Vincent and I have been working through some hypotheses lately, and have one that's rather promising, albeit scary as hell. From our latest measurements pulled from the JWST, we believe that the L3 position from the Sun-Earth relationship coincides with the L3 position of an even larger relationship. It looks to be a mirrored location between the black hole at the center of the Milky Way and something massive out in the Scutum-Crux arm. We have no idea what's out there or why this works—but it just does."

Gilroy perked up. "At the expense of sounding stupid, sir, could you travel into the future?"

"Not stupid at all, son," he replied, honestly. "We don't know. We have tried, but everything ended up in the past. We will just need to wait and see." He winked. "So, we set up protocols, a guidebook on what to do when travelling and how to respond to seeing our future selves should it occur. We formulate an operational plan. We would keep this knowledge to a very small group, pick places in time where we could potentially steer the course of humanity in a different direction, and then go back into the future afterwards to see if and how it worked. And if we didn't like the results, then we'd just go back to right before we originally time-travelled to make said change and try again. Hence why we called it 'Project Save Point.'"

"Like in a video game."

"Precisely," the commander replied. "We have tried so many different options now. We killed Hitler, even baby Hitler at one point. That was... different. We went after Stalin, Mussolini, heck, a few of the guys wanted to kidnap Einstein. But I drew the line at him. Einstein is off-limits. He's just too valuable to our progress overall and I hope we can make it work with him still in the picture. Regardless, it seems like we either have no effect or make it worse. But there's got to be some person or event that we can gently nudge in another direction to avoid the apocalypse."

The radio unit on the wall of the pod scratched to life, jarring both men from their story and back to reality.

"Commander Cavill, Commander Zahn, please report to my ready room at 0800," Captain Filoni's voice emanated from the speaker. "I'd like to finish last night's conversation and go over your latest proposals."

The commander leaned sideways and hit a button. "Roger, sir. See you then."

"What's that all about?" asked Gilroy, despite knowing that it was probably above his paygrade. But, as they didn't use money anymore, he didn't particularly care.

"Eh, he probably doesn't like my latest plan to go after Oppenheimer,"

Cavill replied. "I had a plan that if we got him sick at an early age, with something like dysentery, we could potentially knock him off his academic plans and prevent him from working on the atomic bomb, but without killing him, you know?"

Gilroy visibly gulped. He was still getting used to how nonchalantly his fellow crew members talked about hurting or killing famous people from his childhood history books. It was a weird time to be alive.

"Oh well, it probably won't work anyway," the commander grumbled, rising to his feet. "But we might as well try."

Tim Baird is a Massachusetts-based fantasy and sci-fi author. He enjoys time at home with his family, anything Star Wars related, and being out in the woods of New England. You can learn more about Tim's writing from his website, www.timbaird.us, @timbaird.author on social media, or from your local bookseller.

SLIVERS OF LIGHT

By Belle A. DeCosta

ethany clutched to the vision of his image as one would a ship's railing, desperately trying to keep her emotional boat from capsizing in this unforeseen storm. She looked out over the sea of black and hung on for dear life. So much black. Black suits, black dresses, black mascara smudges under teary eyes. Black, the color of death. *Dead, like Carson.* Like their dreams of retirement, so close and now gone. *Expired, like Carson.*

Bethany took a deep breath and replaced all thoughts with her husband's face. She started to descend the stairs, a grand sweeping staircase Carson had elegantly escorted their daughter down as a bride. Her breath caught at the remembered scene, and she stopped. *Don't think.* She again cleared her mind of all but Carson's reflection and walked into the sea of ebony.

The celebration of her deceased husband's life. Endless air kisses, hand grasping, eye dabbing, sincere yet stifling condolences. All the sorrowful glances and head shakes. After an eternity of treading water through the turbulent whitecaps of socialized grief, the last guests departed, and Bethany kicked off her heels and collapsed into a chair. Her three children, Roland, Charlotte, and Troy, hovered anxiously around, at the ready should she need anything. *What beautiful people we raised, Carson.* She accepted a brandy from her eldest, Roland, fondly touched her daughter Charlotte's belly swollen with child, then shooed them home to comfort their young families. Troy, her youngest, was most reluctant to leave, but she insisted. "I need to be alone," she said.

Once the caterers left and the housekeeper turned in, Bethany took her brandy and drifted into Carson's study. She opened the mahogany double doors and greedily inhaled the air infused with sandalwood cologne, polished wood, worn leather, old books, and the occasional forbidden cigar. The scent of her husband. She heard a mournful whine and found their coonhound Maddie behind the antique mahogany desk. Carson had found the abandoned pup eight years ago in the hospital parking lot, and the two had been constant companions ever since. "Come on, girl," Bethany coaxed, "Let's curl up on the couch and..." And what? Bethany hadn't a clue. How do you continue to breathe when half of you has vanished? Sensing her mistress's growing distress, Maddie padded over and dropped her head into Bethany's lap. Stroking the hound's silken fur, she found comfort in a kindred soul. "We're both untethered, girl, aren't we?"

Bethany lay her head back and closed her eyes. She couldn't remember a time without Carson. They grew up in South Boston in an Irish neighborhood of cops and firemen. Their parents were next-door neighbors and best friends; their fathers were Boston firefighters, and both mothers were at-home moms. Their block-long street dead-ended to an elementary school, and their church sat across the street at the other end. Until junior high, most neighborhood kids never left a four-block radius. A gaggle of kids hung out together, but Bethany and Carson's friendship was closer and unique. They were inseparable from when they were toddlers: even in elementary school when Carson declared girls had cooties and Bethany thought boys were gross. The two never saw one another as boy and girl—they were just them. Both had their first date to the eighth-grade dance with others but spent most of the night hanging out together. Unable to understand why their dates got so angry, they decided the romance thing wasn't worth the trouble and steered clear of dating. Bethany smiled at the memory. *It never occurred to us we might be the romance thing.*

High school brought hormones and proms, and their mindset toward the opposite sex changed. Still, they never thought of each other that way; she was his best bud, and he was her bestie. Carson warned her of the players, and she taught him how to win over a girl. But courtships always ended in break-ups, and neither went steady for long. Occasionally they tried to figure out why but didn't dwell on it—each thought the other was the absolute best, so it must be the other party's issue. Everyone could plainly see jealousy over their closeness was always getting in the way, but the pair never saw it. They were buddies, childhood friends. The idea it was anything more never crossed their minds. Unbeknownst to them at the time, it was everything and then some.

They both were accepted to their college of choice, Bethany to Villanova and Carson to Georgetown. With the excitement of college and pending freedom, awareness didn't hit until that late August morning, saying goodbye. For the first time in their lives, they wouldn't wake up next door to each other in the morning. Bethany remembered feeling the ground shift under her feet at the realization: no Carson for a whole semester. *Is it any wonder the ground has completely given way at my permanent loss of him?* Choking back a sob, she recalled how he looked at her as the unthinkable sank in for him. At that moment, the light finally dawned on both. Carson bent down and kissed her, a kiss tender and heartfelt, shy yet possessive, and oh so right. They stared at one another in awe and adoration, then silently got into their cars and drove away. Neither dared to address it for fear they wouldn't leave. It would take them the entire semester to process the revelation.

*

The cocktail of grief and brandy suddenly hit hard, and Bethany barely made it upstairs to bed. The bed she and Carson had shared for so many years. Where children were conceived, comfort was found and given, birthday breakfasts served, and passion ignited. Now it was just her bed, empty and cold. She threw her clothes on a chair and crinkled her nose. The ensemble reeked of lilies, incense, and earth. *The smell of death.* Bethany shivered and vowed to throw the clothes away in the morning. She crawled under the quilt and braved the desolate darkness of sleep with the memory of their young love blooming fresh in her mind's eye.

The following morning, Bethany stirred, oblivious to the truth for one brief, glorious moment between sleep and wokeness. Then sorrow reignited the throb in her head, anguish gut-punched the air from her lungs, and heartbreak released the dam restraining her tears. She didn't fight back and succumbed to the despair and agony, letting it consume her, welcoming it, hoping it would render her useless. It didn't; it left her limp and ragged, but still able to drag herself into another day. *My new way to start the* day. She did the bare minimum for grooming and headed downstairs to emptiness.

Bethany poured a mug of coffee and sat down at the breakfast nook. *Alone.* She looked out over their perennial gardens and sweeping pastures lined with old stone walls. Having them authentically repaired and restored had cost a fortune but was worth every cent. Carson loved looking out over the land while he drank his first cup of coffee. "A beautiful vision to carry through the day," he'd say. *Used to say but would no more.* She staved off the tears, blurring her view with memories of morning coffee shared in earlier times.

*

Christmas break confirmed what the kiss had intuited, and you couldn't fit a piece of paper between them for six weeks. They met at the diner every morning for coffee, lingering so long they had to run to catch the bus to seasonal jobs. Dinner was at either parent's house, followed by (if they were lucky) some alone time. Privacy was a tricky business with siblings that missed them and mothers that hovered. It usually meant taking a walk or, if one of them had a little extra cash for gas, a ride along Storrow Drive. Bethany smiled, remembering how they could barely keep their hands off one another, but since it was winter in New England and they both lived at home, having sex was a challenge. It usually happened in the backseat of one of their cars, fast and furious, fully clothed, and with pants around their ankles to beat the bitter cold. Carson used to joke his ass was frostbitten, so Bethany gave him a bun warmer for Christmas. They laughed 'til they cried, and it sits on their kitchen counter to this day.

Both knew wasting the remainder of the year's scholarship was not an option and were committed to their respective schools until June. They decided Carson would apply for transfer to Boston University for pre-med and Bethany to Boston College for pre-law. Bethany touched her ear, remembering the hours-long phone calls. *In hindsight, we probably spent more on long-distance phone bills than we saved on tuition.* It all worked out as planned, and that summer, they rented a third-floor walk-up in the Allston Brighton area of Boston, home to tenements full of college students. It was a closet-sized dump with little heat and only enough hot water for one shower — something they didn't mind. Like the diner over break, they made a point to have the first cup of coffee each day together. It was instant coffee, powdered creamer, and stolen sugar packets from the diner, a far cry from the fresh ground Arabica bean brew she was savoring now. The view was fire escapes covered in pigeon droppings and trash piled up on the curb below, instead of gardens and land, but the quality company and conversation were the same, and she loved they'd carried the morning habit through the years.

*

Bethany sighed, brought her mug to the sink, and went in search of something to do. She'd cleared her court calendar for six weeks, knowing her focus would be elsewhere, if anywhere. As a family court judge, she ruled on children's futures, a responsibility she took in earnest. Maddie brought over her leash and sat staring with her soulful hound dog eyes, providing her mistress a task. Carson took her for a run most mornings before making his rounds, a labor of love that now fell on Bethany. "Good idea, girl, the fresh air will do us both good." It took the dog a block or two before she understood her mistress walked, not jog, but they soon settled into a compatible gait. Unfortunately, Bethany's mind chose to travel down a desolate dark path instead of staying on the sunny walk Maddie was enjoying. She was a lawyer, analytical by trade, and a judge who looked at the facts and achieved fair outcomes. But the harder she tried to make sense of Carson's death, the less clear it became and so unfair. Carson was a good man, father, husband, and son. He was a heart surgeon, for Chrissake. He ate right, exercised, and lived a healthy lifestyle. How is it they found him dead of a heart attack on the locker room floor of the Tennis Club? Bethany froze. It was the first time she'd let the horrible vision settle inside her. She started to run, trying to outpace the unfathomable scene in her mind. It worked. Arriving home on shaky legs, it took all her focus to fill her lungs with air.

*

Days turned into weeks, and Bethany unknowingly continued to replace unbearable loneliness and insurmountable sorrow with memories.

The first time the housekeeper changed the sheets, it hit her; Carson would never sleep on them. She lay in the crisp linen and revisited times of laughter and family pajama parties that left her smiling. Likewise, when the nights felt endless and the bed barren, Bethany would conjure up thoughts of lovemaking and long talks snuggled in Carson's protective arms, which offered her rest, if not sleep. Or she'd fondly remember the first days in the closet dump, out of the cramped backseat and onto an air mattress, able to explore each other's bodies and fully appreciate their physical connection.

Her morning coffee became a time to reflect on past conversations. In the small college dump, dreaming of the life that awaited them, loving the life they had. Solving the world's problems or quizzing each other before an exam. Giving pep talks when the grind of school and work threatened to overwhelm one of them. And in this magnificent home, sharing days of law and surgery, and later, their children. Always there for each other.

Bethany made a point to start concentrating on her surroundings during her and Maddie's walks instead of thinking. They lived on the border of Norwell and Scituate, MA, both affluent towns on Boston's South Shore. Under 30 miles from the city, they were a lifestyle away. Norwell offered stately homes restored to their previous grandeur, rolling pastures, and wealthy neighborhoods. Scituate was an upscale coastal town with an old charm feel. Being on the border offered her the best both had to give. She and Maddie walked beautiful treelined streets, admiring the immaculate properties with the scent of the sea in the air. The fresh air was a balm for her mind's tangled cobwebs and splintered heart. Sometimes, if the wind wasn't too bad, Bethany bundled up and walked the dog down to the beach.

On a particularly gray day, returning from one such walk, Bethany stopped to admire their home from the street. "It's quite magnificent, Maddie, isn't it?" Behind a half-acre of a pristine lawn, their historic, rambling farmhouse sat in all its splendor. Fully restored, the white home with oversized windows dressed in classic black shutters was embraced by a wraparound porch and accessorized with a front door of cranberry red. It was precisely what she'd envisioned when she first saw it all those years ago. The gray sky blackened, and driving sleet sent the pair scrambling for cover. Once tucked in with the fireplace lit and a cup of tea, Bethany continued to reminisce.

*

As a young couple, whenever they needed a short break, they'd ride to the South Shore to clear their minds before hitting the books again. Driving along scenic Rte.123 one afternoon, Bethany spotted the property and asked Carson to pull over. "That's where we're going to raise our children one day," she announced. Seeing nothing but a dilapidated, abandoned farmhouse, he laughed. "I'm serious, Carson; that will be our home." For Bethany, it was love at first sight; for Carson, it took a few more drives. *Like a hundred,* she thought and smiled wistfully. Eventually, she won him over, and dreams of restoring the place got them through the grueling pace of studying for boards, clerkship, and residency.

Looking back, she wondered what the college kids thought of the successful doctor and lawyer living on the third floor. But both were raised by practical working-class parents, so they decided to remain where they were until they paid down their student debt. It allowed them to put most of their lucrative salaries towards loans and start the next leg of their life's journey financially sound.

Bethany paid little attention to money; she had the career she'd always wanted and Carson by her side. So, when she came home late one evening to a candlelit takeout dinner on the coffee table, she feared she'd forgotten an important date. Carson handed her a gift wrap box containing an old fashion key and declared her the mistress of their new castle, such as it was.

Almost debt-free, homeowners, and careers on track, Bethany and Carson decided it was time to get married. They were wed in the church at the top of their childhood street, surrounded by life-long friends and neighbors and family members galore. Both members of large Irish Catholic families, there was no way it would be anything less than an event. The reception, planned by their mothers, was an elaborate affair, far beyond what the couple wanted. But seeing the joy it brought their parents was worth the concession. After the wedding, the newlyweds moved from the closet-sized dump and into a 2,800-square-foot money pit.

The original plan of doing some of the renovations themselves didn't last a year. The pair realized they were in over their heads between lack of time and zero skill. Bethany cringed at the memory of living in a construction zone for two years. Carson had joked the only way they survived it was the long hours they worked. But the end result was worth every cent spent and any inconvenience suffered. Through the years, they continued to add personal touches, making it their homestead.

Bethany looked around at the pieces of their life together, evident in pictures, décor, worn mementos, and the warm scent of home. She wandered through each room, viewing it anew through the different lenses of time: as a new bride, part of a carefree couple, a young mother, a saddened momma bird in an empty nest, a secure middle-aged woman, and now as a widow. Love was the one constant this beautiful space held dear and kept all those years. And Carson was the core of that love. That was his legacy. Death had taken Carson's physical being but not his presence. That lived on in these walls, her heart, her thoughts, their family, and her life. Bethany now understood Carson, a part of her soul since birth, would remain with her in their life-long memories and love. Death could not break an eternal bond.

The widow looked out the window and saw rays of light breaking through the dark sky. *Like the light of memories penetrates through the blackness of my grief.* Bethany knew her time of mourning was not over, her cracked existence far from repaired. But in this darkest of times, she now saw a glimmer of light to guide and help heal her. Inspired, Bethany went to invite her children and grandchildren over for dinner. She was ready to start adding her own slivers of light.

Belle A. DeCosta's work includes her memoir, *Echoes in the Mirror*, a novel, *Treading Water* (awarded Finalist for Best First Novel by Next Generations Indie Book Awards 2022), and *The Heart of Addisen*, book two of the *Treading Water* series. She has been featured in previous ARIA Anthologies, and makes her home in East Providence.

Made in the USA
Middletown, DE
03 September 2023

37626855R00169